# Drug Abuse in Sport

## ISSUES
### (previously Issues for the Nineties)

## Volume 26

Editor

Craig Donnellan

First published by Independence
PO Box 295
Cambridge CB1 3XP
England

**British Library Cataloguing in Publication Data**
Drug Abuse in Sport – (Issues Series)
I. Donnellan, Craig II. Series
362.2'93'088'796


ISBN 1 86168 045 7


**Printed in Great Britain**
City Print Ltd
Milton Keynes


**Typeset by**
Claire Boyd


**Cover**
The illustration on the front cover is by
Andrew Smith.

# CONTENTS

# Introduction

*Drug Abuse in Sport* is the twenty-sixth volume in the series: **Issues**. The aim of this series is to offer up-to-date information about important issues in our world.

*Drug Abuse in Sport* looks at drug abuse in sport and drugs testing.

The information comes from a wide variety of sources and includes:
Government reports and statistics
Newspaper reports and features
Magazine articles and surveys
Literature from lobby groups
and charitable organisations.

It is hoped that, as you read about the many aspects of the issues explored in this book, you will critically evaluate the information presented. It is important that you decide whether you are being presented with facts or opinions. Does the writer give a biased or an unbiased report? If an opinion is being expressed, do you agree with the writer?

*Drug Abuse in Sport* offers a useful starting-point for those who need convenient access to information about the many issues involved. However, it is only a starting-point. At the back of the book is a list of organisations which you may want to contact for further information.

*****

# Consider the consequences

**Some information from the Football Association about drugs and their effects**

- All drug use has a risk to health.
- All have a risk to behaviour and/ or performance.
- Use of many drugs is illegal. This also applies to cigarettes and alcohol if you are under 16.
- Any so-called 'benefits' or enjoyment from using an illegal or performance-enhancing drug or cigarettes are outweighed by the risks to health, performance and your future in football.
- If in doubt, don't!
- It is not 'big' or 'grown up' to use drugs.
- By training, hard work, and skill, be good enough without drugs.
- Footballers are athletes and athletes and drugs do not go together!

### Tobacco
As in cigarettes, cigars, pipes.

*What harm can it do?*
Bad breath – Shortness of breath – Chest, lung or bronchial problems – Bad cough – Can result in cancer, heart disease.

*Suitable for footballers?*
No – not if you value your health, fitness. Why waste it?

### Alcohol
As in beer, wines, spirits

*What harm can it do?*
Unless used sensibly and responsibly use can result in: headaches, sickness, loss of control over behaviour, e.g. Effects the ability to think or act clearly when driving. Long-term heavy use can result in serious health problems.

*Suitable for footballers?*
Not if you are under age – you are breaking the law. Also it can cause problems for your health and fitness and ability to think and act clearly. Celebrate your success by all means, but in moderation and off the pitch!

### Solvents
As in glue, aerosol, correcting fluids, butane gas.

*What harm can it do?*
Can cause death on first use. Also long-term damage possible from effects on throat and other organs. Many dangerous risks from the poisons in solvents, from the ways they are sniffed, and from the behaviour they can cause.

*Suitable for footballers?*
No – the health risks are not worth it and they can't help your football, but they can hinder it.

### Drugs in sport
As in performance-enhancing drugs, anabolic steroids, etc. various tablets, pills and injectable liquids.

*What harm can it do?*
Unless prescribed, use can result in serious health problems. Particularly effects heart disease, liver function and sexual organs. Some other side-effects such as acne can also be unpleasant.

*Suitable for footballers?*
No – using these drugs can result in being banned from playing. It is also cheating! You may not only be harming yourself but also the sport of football.

### Cannabis
As in dope, grass, weed, marijuana.

*What harm can it do?*
Can make you behave as if you are drunk. This, as with alcohol and solvents, reduces your control over your behaviour and memory. Long-term use has the risk of causing health problems such as bronchitis.

*Suitable for footballers?*
No – use is illegal and it could have a negative effect on your health and behaviour as well as your career in football.

### Other illegal drugs
As in heroin, cocaine, LSD, amphetamines, crack, ecstasy.

*What harm can it do?*
Can be in various forms, powders, pills etc. according to the drug in question – There could be much harm from using any of these substances – and never mix drugs. They effect your health, behaviour and can harm your relationships with your friends and family.

*Suitable for footballers?*
No: illegal drugs can be very dangerous. Your performance as a player could suffer and your career with any club would be at very serious risk.

• The above is an extract from *Fit for Football*, produced by the Football Association. See page 41 for address details. © *Football Association*

# The medical effects of steroid abuse

## By Prof. R. V. Brooks

### What is a side-effect?

The anabolic steroids are taken in the hope that they will improve strength and performance but they may have other, unwanted effects. Some of these 'unwanted effects' may not, strictly speaking, be side-effects but merely the normal action of a hormone when present in higher concentrations than is appropriate. For example, women and children normally produce small amounts of the male hormone testosterone naturally. If they then take additional male hormone it will have undesirable masculinising effects, inappropriate for their gender or age.

Other undesirable effects, however, may indeed be 'side-effects' due to structural modification of the male hormone for a particular purpose. Examples of this are the modifications necessary to make the male hormone active when taken by mouth. Such modifications protect the hormone from destruction in the gut but at the same time also make the steroid somewhat toxic to the liver. Yet other side-effects may be due to metabolites of the hormone rather than to the male steroid itself. Not all anabolic steroids are metabolised in the same way. For example some, but not all, the anabolic steroids are metabolised in part to oestrogens and can cause both feminising and masculinising effects. In such cases male breast enlargement may be seen (gynaecomastia).

### Normal action of testosterone

To understand the way in which the unwanted effects of steroid abuse may arise, it is helpful to consider the normal action of the natural male hormone. Testosterone has two sorts of action: these are called androgenic and anabolic. By its androgenic actions, testosterone has masculinising effects on the growth of hair on face and body, on the pitch of voice and effects on behaviour by increasing competitiveness and aggression. Apart from these androgenic effects, testosterone also has an anabolic effect by which it causes growth of the muscles. The chemical modifications in the structure of synthetic anabolic steroids are designed to increase the anabolic effect relative to the androgenic effect. However, scientific studies have indicated that it is unlikely that these steroids have any direct anabolic or growth promoting effect on the muscles of adult men. It seems likely that any beneficial effect on the performance of adult men results from the androgenic properties of the steroid acting via the central nervous system in

*Anabolic steroids are taken in the hope that they will improve strength and performance but they may have other, unwanted effects*

increasing competitiveness. It may be that the subject is able to train harder and for longer periods of time when on the anabolic steroid and that it is this increased training which is responsible for any improvement in performance.

### Harmful effects on women and children

In young athletes and women, and these are the groups whose performance is likely to benefit most from the action of the male hormone, masculinisation is likely to be a major problem. In women, hair growth on the face and body may follow the male pattern and there may be acne, irreversible voice changes and serious disturbances of the menstrual cycle.

#### Juveniles

In young people there may be stunting of growth. Anabolic steroids stimulate growth of the long bones by causing new bone to be laid down at either end of the bone shaft. However, the steroid has an even greater effect on the plates of cartilage separating the shaft from the head of the bone. It causes these plates of

cartilage, the epiphyseal plates, to be converted into bone. Once this process is completed no further growth in length is possible. Because they cause early fusion of these plates, the steroids can consequently cause stunting of growth.

*Adult men*

It might be thought that adult males would not be harmed by extra androgen. However the control of the testes by the pituitary gland may be disturbed, resulting in infertility. The testes are stimulated to secrete testosterone by luteinizing hormone (LH) produced by the pituitary gland at the base of the brain. The secretion of LH is, in turn, controlled by the concentration of testosterone in the blood which feeds back on the pituitary inhibiting LH secretion: this simple feedback mechanism tends to keep the concentration of testosterone fairly constant. It is rather like a thermostat regulating a domestic central heating system. If you, therefore, administer testosterone or an anabolic steroid to a normal man, the secretion of LH by the pituitary and of testosterone by the testes will be suppressed. Another pituitary hormone will also be suppressed, that is follicle stimulating hormone (FSH), which controls spermatogenesis. Anabolic steroid administration may, therefore, result in reduced sperm count and infertility. This reduced sperm count may persist for three months or longer after stopping the steroid administration. Adult males may also experience increased facial and body hair, acne, deepening voice, enlargement of the prostate and an acceleration of male pattern baldness.

## Additional hazards of orally active anabolic steroids

As mentioned earlier, synthetic anabolic steroids given by mouth can have harmful effects on liver function and jaundice may result. A more serious consequence is liver cancer. Over the years many cases of liver cancer have been reported in patients suffering from various diseases who have been treated with orally active anabolic steroids for prolonged periods of time. In the last ten years a number of such cases have been reported from athletes and body-builders who have used steroids of this type. There has also been an association of anabolic steroids with the extremely rare Wilms tumour – a type of kidney cancer.

## Long-term hazards

Rare conditions, such as liver cancer in young men or the Wilms tumour, are not difficult to link with the use of anabolic steroids. I believe a greater risk from steroid doping and one not confined to the oral steroids, is from coronary heart disease. It is, however, much more difficult to prove a causal long-term relationship with a common disease. Nevertheless, there are clear indications that a link between the use of anabolic steroids and heart disease is likely. The administration of anabolic steroids to athletes is now known to cause changes in the fatty substances (lipoproteins) in the blood which are characteristic of those seen in groups with a greater risk of developing coronary heart disease.

## Can steroids be used safely?

It has often been suggested that the use of anabolic steroids in sport would be safe if they were taken only under medical supervision. This, of course, was the way in which they were used in the German Democratic Republic and we now know how unsafe that procedure was. Indeed, it is doubtful if any amount of the male hormone is without risk. Published comparisons of the duration of life of eunuchs and intact men in a Kansas Institute for mental defectives suggest that even the normal amounts of testosterone secreted naturally, subject to the checks and balances of the endocrine system, carry a heavy penalty in life expectancy.

More information regarding long-term consequences of anabolic steroid abuse should emerge eventually from studies now under way.

## Summary

1  Anabolic steroids taken by mouth are harmful to the liver. They may cause jaundice and occasionally liver cancer.
2  Anabolic steroids administered to juveniles may cause stunting of growth.
3  Anabolic steroids, both natural and synthetic, may result in masculinisation in women and leave juveniles with acne, growth of facial and body hair and with permanent voice changes.
4  Women usually experience menstrual irregularities and may also have clitoral enlargement and male pattern baldness.
5  Adult males may suffer complete suppression of sperm production (and therefore be infertile) during and for some months after treatment with both natural and synthetic anabolic steroids.
6  Prolonged administration to adult males may result in an increase of facial and body hair, but a thinning of scalp hair, and prostate enlargement. A deepening of the pitch of voice may be noticed and some steroids may cause breast enlargement (gynaecomastia).
7  A variety of miscellaneous effects is sometimes reported in both sexes receiving anabolic steroids. These include gastrointestinal disorders (oral steroids only), muscle cramps and spasms, sleeplessness, headache, dizziness, faintness, lethargy, water retention, drowsiness and nose bleeds. There may also be skin rash or local reaction at the site of injection.
8  Quantitatively the most serious unwanted effects of anabolic steroid treatment would appear to be those related to changes in the fatty substances in the blood. These changes may have serious long-term consequences on the liability to heart attacks and strokes.
9  Rarely fatal kidney cancers (Wilms tumours) have been associated with anabolic steroid use.
10 Because of the effects on the central nervous system there may be alternations in libido and aggressive behavioural changes.

• The above article first appeared in *Coaching Focus* No. 23 and is reproduced by kind permission of the NCF. See page 41 for address details.
© *National Coaching Foundation (NCF) Summer 1993*

# Drugs, doping and young people

**Drugs in sport is an emotive, complex and ever-changing issue. Where young, aspiring sports people are involved, there is a need for responsible action to prevent them from even testing the water**

In Scotland, drug abuse in sport is not a major problem but there is no room for complacency. Everyone involved in youth sport must be aware of the issues and be prepared to take responsibility for information and education on the topic. Young people must also assume responsibility.

No single reason can explain the misuse of drugs by young sports people. A contributing factor may be the pressure exerted on them to improve their performance for financial reward, status, political ideology, kudos or the attainment of unrealistic targets. The pressure can be applied, either directly or indirectly, by fellow competitors, family, coaches, sponsors, the public and the media.

## Prevention

Positive steps can be taken, though, to prevent young sports people from using performance-enhancing drugs. With parents, peers, governing body officials and coaches working together, an early prevention strategy is possible. Such a strategy should include:

- Good nutritional advice.
- The opportunity to play sport as well as to compete.
- Reduced parental/coach pressure.
- Reduced personal pressure through the setting of realistic targets.
- Monitored training programmes, with open discussion on preparation, relaxation and injuries.
- Realistic approaches to medical conditions, particularly when returning to training following injury or illness.
- Suitable, positive role models and emphasis on the healthy lifestyle required to maintain performance.
- The development of coping skills to face failure and success.
- A stable and supportive environment which cares for the individual.
- A clear policy with respect to the image of the sport, the club and the athlete, including the means to deal with those who break the rules (not only punishment, but rehabilitation).

## A need for caution

There are certain medications, both over the counter and on prescription, which may contain banned substances. Elite young sports people must be well informed and ensure that they do not take medication for a common ailment which may contain a banned substance. Sportsmen or sportswomen in any doubts as to whether a substance is banned must check with their pharmacist or a general practitioner and/or governing body to ensure that they are not inadvertently breaking their sport's rules.

It is a common assumption that there is a specific and definitive list of banned drugs. This is not the case. The International Olympic Committee (IOC) goes some way to solving this problem by issuing a list of banned classes of drugs, as opposed to a list of the banned drugs themselves which would contain literally thousands of entries.

## Support material

Doping control advice cards and general information packs are available and in the coming year the Sports Councils, in conjunction with governing bodies of sport, are hoping to publish a competitors' handbook and offer information seminars to governing body squads.

- If you would like further information, please contact your governing body or the Scottish Sports Council. See page 41 for address details.

*© Arena*
*April, 1995*

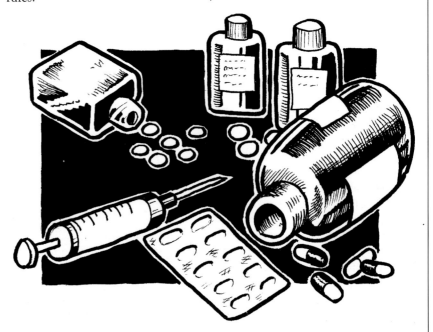

# Drug cheats still one lap ahead

They were supposed to be the latest hi-tech weaponry in the chemical warfare against doping. But after more than a week of the Atlanta Olympics, no positive drug samples had shown up on the £300,000 high-resolution spectrometers. In fact, the athlete generating the most news was the one who was confirmed as having passed her test.

With so much speculation over Michelle Smith's astonishing success at these Games, the International Olympic Committee were forced to acknowledge last week that all the swimmers tested the previous Saturday had passed. That included the Irish swimmer, whose gold medals had drawn suspicion from all quarters.

The sophisticated new machines, which test urine samples, are supposed to be three times more sensitive than those used at the Barcelona Olympics; it is claimed they can detect substances in the body several months after being taken.

The IOC campaigned for the new spectrometers following their high success rate at the laboratory in Cologne, which caught 56 of the 64 weightlifters found guilty of doping in 1995. However, a recent secret report claims that the machine is not as effective as they first thought.

'The spectrometers can increase the period of detection for four specific steroids for up to one week, and these are not the drugs of choice among athletes,' it said. It once again suggested that the drug cheats are one step ahead of the testers.

The most popular substances at these Games are believed to be:

## Human growth hormone

A synthetic substance which is known as the 'drug of champions' because so many of the top sprinters are suspected of using it. It was originally developed to combat dwarfism.
*Advantages*: Has the same effects as anabolic steroids, but is totally undetectable, because, while the IOC ban it, they have been unable to devise a procedure to test for it.
*Disadvantages*: Cost – £1,300 for a 10-day course.
*Distinguishing features*: Gives users a distinctive jutting jaw.
*Users*: Sprinters, swimmers.

## Anabolic steroids

The old favourite, and still the most popular drug on the market among athletes.
*Advantages*: Easy to obtain and relatively cheap. It is also known to work. New steroids can be rubbed into the skin rather than injected or taken orally.
*Disadvantages*: Most easily detectable of all drugs. Suspicion that they might cause cancer in later life.
*Distinguishing features*: Athletes are muscle-bound and tend to be very aggressive, with wild mood swings.
*Users*: Athletes, swimmers, boxers, weightlifters.

## EPO

Popular among distance runners because it mimics the effects of altitude training and blood doping. Used by doctors to treat patients with kidney problems.
*Advantages*: Currently undetectable and known to have impressive benefits in increasing endurance.
*Disadvantages*: The IOC will almost certainly have a test for it by the time of the next Games in Sydney. More worryingly, in hot conditions, such as Atlanta, it can kill if it is not taken in the correct dosage. Several cyclists have already died around the world.
*Distinguishing features*: Gives users pinched features, particularly around the cheekbones.
*Users*: Distance runners, cyclists.

## Stimulants

These include cocaine and ephedrine.
*Advantages*: Enable athletes to have a quick fix immediately before competition. Some athletes believe they act as a masking agent for anabolic steroids, although many experts disagree.
*Disadvantages*: Tend to be easily detectable. Ephedrine is found in over-the-counter cold cures and can trigger mistaken positives. No long-term benefit.
*Distinguishing features*: None.
*Users*: Athletes, swimmers, cyclists, boxers, weightlifters.

## Beta blockers

Popular among athletes needing precision and calm nerves.
*Advantages*: Reduces hand tremors and calms the nervous system.
*Disadvantages*: Reduces levels of oxygen in the blood.
*Distinguishing features*: None.
*Users*: Shooters, archers, divers.

© The Observer
July, 1997

# The Mr Cleans face an uphill struggle

By Michael Thompson-Noel

There are good reasons why many drugs are banned in sport. But as the stakes for which sports stars compete spiral higher, the anti-drugs argument is being portrayed as archaic, mainly because it is now said to be impossible to tell who is 'clean' and who is not.

Sebastian Coe, the great British runner and world record holder, has been a lifelong enemy of the druggies, and of the biochemists, doctors, coaches and pushers who assist them.

'There are three big objections to drug-taking,' Coe once told me. 'It's morally wrong – cheating. It's dangerous – people die. And it's unnecessary. Unfortunately, the more sophisticated science gets the more people will be drawn to drugs. We are having to deal with sci-fi chemists who are given a full-time remit to work on better and more undetectable drugs. There is no alternative but to ban for life an athlete who is positively tested.'

That was nine years ago, when Coe was still a track star. Since then, things have got blurrier and more complicated, with the biochemists said to be easily outpacing the sports drugs police. As a result, there are those who maintain that all drugs will have to be legalised if the does-he-doesn't-he debate is to subside.

Dr John Hawley, director of the high-performance laboratory at the South African Sports Science Institute in Cape Town, is one of those who claims it is no longer possible to tell who is 'clean'. In the September issue of SA Sports Illustrated Hawley says that whenever a medal winner stands on a podium these days, he doesn't know whether it is the athlete or his or her drugs that are being saluted.

'You can't ignore it,' says Hawley. 'There's no question that drugs are a big part of today's superior performances. I'm not going to mention any names, but you look at the physiques of those guys: you just don't get pectoral muscles like that from huge bench presses. In the strength and power events I would say that as many as 50 per cent of competitors at the Olympics have used performance-enhancing drugs, maybe more.'

> *. . . it is now said to be impossible to tell who is 'clean' and who is not*

Perhaps, says Hawley, the only way forward is to legalise the use of steroids and all other enhancers. 'Maybe we should just make steroids legal. As unethical and as morally wrong as it sounds, I actually think that's the way to go.' That is not an original suggestion. But it is becoming harder for sports authorities to brush it aside as eccentric.

Primo Nebiolo, president of the International Amateur Athletics Federation (the word 'amateur' in its name is almost wilfully anachronistic), said last week that athletes who break world records at next year's world (outdoor) championships in Athens would receive a £66,000 bonus. Nebiolo said he had the backing of a sponsor, and that he hoped similar bonuses would be on offer for world records at the world indoor championships, World Cup and IAAF grand prix final.

At present, athletics' richest prizes are those at the privately sponsored Zurich grand prix meeting, which has a budget of £4m and offers bonuses of £33,000 for world records.

All this prize money is unlikely to encourage athletics stars to fling their pills and potions out of their speeding Mercedes. And here is another thing. Track records (even for the 50km walk) are measured in hundredths of a second. Could I be the only person in the world to imagine that some biochemist is dreaming of a way to lower a world record by 0.01 or 0.02 of a second in a dozen consecutive races? Surely not.

© *The Financial Times, August, 1997*

Ken Pyne

# How drug runners slip through the net

**Duncan Mackay discovers a computer link to the tangled web of dope trafficking in sport**

The Olympic athlete sat in front of his personal computer and dialled a telephone number on his modem. Within seconds, he was connected to an Internet site that offered him the most sophisticated drugs on the market.

'Dear Friend and Fellow Athlete' appeared on his screen. 'Today, like never before, elite bodybuilders, top models, world-class athletes . . . are safely using anabolic steroids and other performance-enhancement substances to achieve superior results.'

It goes on to describe the use of human growth hormone, including the new advanced strain of the undetectable substance IGF-1, and anabolic steroids. It also tells you how to take them. Revealed exactly are the number of days that athletes must stop taking a particular drug in order to avoid detection during competition.

For $30, it is possible to order a two-week supply of a steroid such as Oxandrolone – originally developed as a treatment for AIDS – which helps promote strength and muscular hardness. According to the on-screen dealer, its effectiveness rating for sportsmen is eight on a scale of ten. Oxandrolone is one of only several banned substances it is possible to have delivered to your home.

For years, dope testers have complained they have been playing a game of catch-up with the drugs cheat. This latest use of the information superhighway leaves the testers further adrift. The Internet is replacing the doper's bible, *The Underground Steroid Handbook*, which was readily available in the Olympic village in Barcelona five years ago – but at a price.

The secret publishers used red paper to avoid photocopying. They no longer need to take that pre-caution, because for a small fee, charged directly to a credit card, the information is now available on a world-wide web site.

In Atlanta, anti-doping officials were armed with the stealth bomber of their profession – the high-resolution mass spectrometer, a $300,000 machine that is claimed can detect drug residue in much smaller proportions than previous testing methods. Three of the machines that were installed in the Atlanta lab were used at the world weightlifting championships last year with dramatic results; drug positives in 6.2 per cent of the samples tested, compared with 0.85 per cent the year before.

The IOC ordered the Atlanta Committee for the Olympic Games to use the mass spectrometers. ACOG repeatedly voiced objections, leading to speculation – vehemently denied – that those in charge feared too many drug positives and that a label of the 'Doping Games' would overshadow all else.

The late installation of the new machinery delayed accreditation of the Atlanta lab, and final clearance was obtained only this week. That

---

## Hidden costs to drug cheats

### Main types of banned substances – the 'benefits' and the long-term side effects

**Stimulants**
**Examples:** Amphetamine, Cocaine
**Gains:** Increased mental and physical stimulation, alertness and competitiveness
**Dangers:** Raised blood pressure. Irregular heartbeat. Addiction.

**Narcotic Analgesics**
**Example:** Methadone
**Gains:** Mask injuries or illness and increase pain threshold.
**Dangers:** Aggravation of injury with added risk of permanent damage. Respiratory problems

**Anabolic Agents**
**Example:** Testosterone
**Gains:** Increased strength, endurance and muscle growth.
**Dangers and side effects:**
Males: Heightened aggression, impotence, kidney damage, baldness, development of breasts.
Females: Increased aggression, development of male features, facial and body hair. Irregular periods.

**Beta-blockers**
**Examples:** Atenolol, Oxprenolol
**Gains:** Relax nerves and stop trembling by reducing heart rate and blood pressure.
**Dangers:** Low blood pressure, slow heart rate, tiredness

**Peptide Hormones, Analogues**
**Examples:** Chorionic, Gonadotophin, EPO
**Gains:** Pain control, repair of body tissue. Improved oxygen flow and muscle growth.
**Dangers:** Abnormal growth of hands, feet, face and internal organs. Blood clots, adding risk of stroke

**Blood Doping**
Blood is injected into the body to increase number of blood cells. More commonly used by competitors in endurance events.
**Gains:** Increased red blood cells feed more oxygen to muscles, boosting energy levels.
**Dangers:** Allergic reactions, infections/clotting, overload of circulatory system. Kidney damage.

*Erythropoietin (EPO) has similar characteristics and may be used as an alternative but carries added risk of overloading heart.*

**Diuretics**
**Examples:** Frusemide, Triameterine
Diuretics have two main functions:
1. Rapid weight loss
2. Urine passed more quickly – believed to make detection of other drugs more difficult.
**Dangers:** Dehydration, cramps, dizziness, headaches and nausea.

*UK Sports Council*

could pose a problem if a drug test is challenged; part of the defence of test procedures usually includes a lab's track record, and the Olympic lab in Atlanta won't have one.

But Dr Jean-Pierre de Mondenard, a French expert on performance-enhancing drugs, who has recently written a book on the subject, has called the machines only 'a publicity stunt to cover up the immense failings of the doping controls'. He said the devices were useful only for detecting anabolic steroids, but totally ineffective in uncovering the use of synthetic hormones that are similar to those naturally produced by the body. Even IOC officials admit that there is still no means of testing for EPO, the blood-doping drug, or human growth hormone – the two substances most popular among elite athletes these days.

De Mondenard says a 'virtual mafia' is operating within high-

performance sports, including large com-panies and major pharma-ceutical laboratories. 'These are very expensive products,' he said. 'There are doctors, chemists, pharmacists and laboratories that make millions in trafficking them. There are cases of sponsors who pay for these "cures" for the athletes they sponsor or obtain the synthetic hormones they need.'

© The Observer
July, 1996

# Scientist supports legalising steroids

A leading South African sports scientist has said drugs should be legalised in sport to end the 'does he, doesn't he?' debate once and for all.

Dr John Hawley, director of the High Performance laboratory at the South African Sports Science Institute in Cape Town, was quoted in the September issue of SA Sports Illustrated as saying it was no longer possible to tell who was 'clean' and who was not.

He said many athletes at the Atlanta Olympics have had to make a choice of whether they are going to take performance-enhancing drugs. 'Whenever anyone stands up there on the podium I don't know whether it's them or the drugs,' Hawley said.

'You can't ignore it. There's no question that drugs are a big part of today's superior performances.

'I'm not going to mention any names but you look at the physiques of those guys . . . you just don't get pectoral muscles like that from huge bench presses.

'In the strength and power events I would say that as many as 50 per cent of competitors at the Olympics have used performance-enhancing drugs, maybe more.'

He said the only way to recreate a level playing-field was to consider legalising the use of steroids.

'Maybe we should just make steroids legal. As unethical and as morally wrong as it sounds I actually think that's the way to go.

'It's an ethical problem. There's

---

**'If you are asking me what are the limits to human performance, we have already surpassed them. Most of these are drug records'**

---

no question where I or anyone else at this institute stand medically – steroids are illegal and performance-enhancing.'

He claimed Atlanta's highly publicised doping laboratory had been a public relations exercise. 'The public has been whitewashed into thinking that drugs enhance athletes the week before competition – they don't. Steroids help in training in the winter months long before the competitions.' Hawley said.

'If an athlete stops using steroids three months before competition they won't be detected.'

Hawley had been asked to theorise on how low world records would ultimately fall.

'If you are asking me what are the limits to human performance, we have already surpassed them. Most of these are drug records.'

© The Independent
August, 1997

# How an innocent lunchtime bagel could ruin a promising career

*By Charles Arthur,*
*Science Editor*

Faulty testing for drugs could lead to people being turned down unfairly for jobs, according to the scientist who proved the athlete Diane Modahl was innocent of taking steroids.

John Honour, of University College London, said that the Government should act now to set standards for drug testing, to avoid injustices against innocent people whose samples test positive. Testing for use of drugs such as cannabis, heroin and cocaine is one of the fastest-growing commercial areas in the UK.

Dr Honour told *The Independent*: 'There aren't any standards for positive tests or for how the tests should be done . . . If you failed a pre-employment test you might not even hear – you'd just not get offered the job.'

A growing number of organisations, including Shell, BP, the Prisons Service, banks and British Rail have recently introduced random testing, and a number of companies – including Shell – ask applicants for some jobs to undergo drugs tests.

Dr Honour, of the Department of Molecular Pathology, has 25 years' experience in testing urine samples for steroids. In 1994 he began examining the tests carried out by a Spanish laboratory on the sealed urine sample provided by Ms Modahl.

That had shown a high level of breakdown produces – metabolites – from the male hormone testosterone. That implied that Ms Modahl had taken the drug artificially.

But Dr Honour showed that bacteria found in urine could react with normal metabolites to produce testosterone. His evidence was crucial in reversing the August 1994 decision to ban Ms Modahl. Her name was eventually cleared last March.

He argues that similar problems could lurk for would-be employees as the use of drugs testing expands. 'It's known that if you've been eating a bagel with poppy seeds on, you can test positive for opiates – drugs like heroin,' he said. 'The point is, each athletics test costs £100, whereas companies are only paying about £5.'

> **'There aren't any standards for positive tests or for how the tests should be done . . . If you failed a pre-employment test you might not even hear – you'd just not get offered the job.'**

The problem is that there is no clearly agreed standard for the minimum levels of metabolites which indicate the use of particular drugs.

'On the whole, the methods used are less sophisticated than those used by the IAAF, and there is no official regulation of companies that offer the tests,' he said.

Unilabs, a London testing company, said that it was very careful to prevent 'false positive' results. 'We have a two-step procedure, so that if we find something in our first assay tests, we use chromatography and gas spectrometry to look for metabolites,' said Fred Rutherford, head of scientific services.

People who claim innocence in industrial tribunals on drugs charges usually dropped their defence when evidence from Unilabs was presented, he added.

But not everyone adopts stringent standards. Dr Honour suggested that some testing companies might be profiting from the lack of standards in the fast-growing business of drugs testing.

'Most of the people in this area make their money from testing for companies. They do thousands of tests – so they don't want the bad side to come out. They would prop each other up,' he said. © *The Independent February, 1997*

# Anabolic steroids

## Information from the UK Sports Council

### Introduction

Drugs are intended to treat people with medical ailments. Used properly, drugs can save lives. Nevertheless, any drug can be dangerous especially when taken for a long time and in high doses. Doctors take these risks into consideration when prescribing treatments.

Drug taking (or doping) by sportsmen and women in an attempt to improve performance and to gain an unfair advantage has become more widespread. Despite the fact that doping can be dangerous, sportsmen and women (supposedly at the peak of fitness and in good health) are turning to drugs in the belief that drugs will help them to run faster or for longer, to reduce fatigue, or to help build-up muscles. It doesn't seem to matter that there is often little evidence that drugs really do improve performance. Often sportsmen and sportswomen believe they enhance performance and that is also cheating. Sometimes sportsmen and women don't realise what they are taking.

In sport, one class of drugs is abused more frequently than any other – androgenic anabolic steroids.

Let's examine some of the beliefs and facts about the use of androgenic anabolic steroids and their use in sport.

### What are anabolic steroids?

The anabolic steroids used by sportsmen and women are a powerful group of natural or synthetic compounds similar in chemical structure to the natural hormone of the male (testosterone). Testosterone has two types of action:
Androgenic – promoting the development of male characteristics and
Anabolic – stimulating the build-up of muscle tissue.

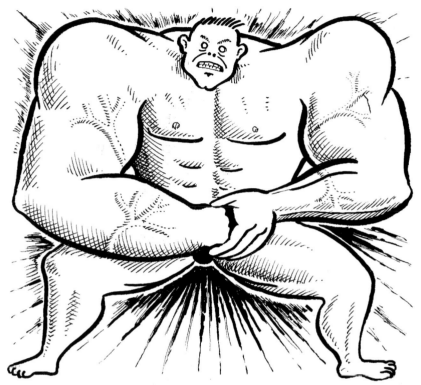

Scientists have been successful in changing the structure of some steroids in order to increase the muscle building properties whilst minimising the masculinising effects. However, all available steroids have both actions but to varying degrees according to the body's own response. **Examples**: There are more than 100 different anabolic steroids available throughout the world. Common examples are nandrolone, stanozolol, testosterone and boldenone. Steroids are available in tablet form or for intramuscular injection, under trade names such as dianabol, durabolin, deca-durabolin, winstrol, and anavar.

### How do they work?

Because of their protein-building properties, anabolic steroids have been used in medicine in the treatment of diseases including;
- Anaemic conditions
- Wasting diseases
- Bone diseases
- Advanced breast cancer

Anabolic steroids are also used under strict medical control as a replacement therapy for boys or men deficient in the natural male hormone.

However, the side-effects which may occur, particularly in long-term use, has restricted their usefulness in medicine.

### Why do sports men and women use steroids?

The practice of taking anabolic steroids began with bodybuilders and weight-lifters in the late 1950s and has gradually spread to athletics and to other sports.

Sportsmen and women take anabolic steroids to improve their performance and in particular:
- To increase their muscle strength
- To train harder and for longer
- To increase their competitiveness

There is little evidence to support the belief that anabolic steroids alone can increase muscle strength in adult males; development is very much dependent upon an appropriate diet and exercise programme. However, studies have shown that muscles tend to look bigger, but this is probably due to water retention.

It is more likely that the androgenic effects of steroids – increased aggression and competitiveness (which makes people train harder and enables them to recover more quickly) – increases strength.

Because of their ability to promote the quality and quantity of training, anabolic steroids have become known as 'training drugs', taken during the training period before a competition. To reduce the risk of being caught by a drugs test, the competitor comes off the drugs a few weeks before a competition and may retain some of the benefits.

## What are the risks?
Some sportsmen and women believe that anabolic steroids can improve their performance and are willing to take the risks associated with using them. Anabolic steroids have many harmful effects, particularly when misused for months or years. Some effects do not disappear when the drug is stopped. These effects are made worse by the stacking (i.e. several types of anabolic Steroid being taken simultaneously) and 'cycling' (i.e. alternating the use of several types of anabolic steroids) and by using high doses, often exceeding the normal medical dose by 5–50 times.

## Liver disorders and heart disease
The most dramatic side-effect of anabolic steroids is the serious damage to liver structure and function leading to jaundice, liver failure, liver tumours and bleeding in the liver. A number of premature deaths have been attributed to anabolic steroid abuse. Recently, a 26-year-old bodybuilder who had been taking anabolic steroids for a number of years died of cancer of the liver.

A former British female bodybuilding champion now has permanent kidney and liver damage due to anabolic steroids abuse.

Of greater quantitative significance are probably the harmful long-term effects on the types of fatty substances in the blood. These changes are likely to cause an increased liability to heart attacks and strokes.

It is thought that steroid abuse can lead to premature heart disease, because the drugs can cause increases in blood pressure and can change the levels of fats in the blood. Increased fats are likely to cause heart attacks.

## Sexual problems and effects on the physique
Men suffer reduced sperm production and sterility. Shrinking and hardening of the testicles, impotence and the growth of breasts can often occur. These changes are probably reversible when steroid use has stopped, but it may be some time before a return to normal.

Females taking steroids may experience disruption of the menstrual cycle and ovulation, changes in the sex organs, balding, acne, growth of facial hair and deepening of the voice. Some of these masculinising changes are irreversible after steroid use has ceased. Anabolic steroids can cause miscarriage, still birth or damage to the foetus, particularly during early pregnancy.

In children and adolescents they affect growth and can lead to stunting.

## Behavioural effects
Steroid abuse can cause changes in behaviour in some individuals. These changes can be very serious. Increased moodiness and aggression can occur that may affect the person's relationships with other people. Depending on the dosages used, the changes in behaviour can be severe enough to meet criteria for psychiatric disorders. Although these behavioural changes are reversible when steroid use ceases, how long this will take could vary from person to person. Furthermore, the psychological changes are noticeable fairly soon after the athlete starts taking the drugs unlike heart disease or liver cancer.

## Summary
These adverse reactions are believed to be dependent upon the amount of steroids used and the length of time over which they are used. It is not possible to predict individual reactions. Although gains in body weight, muscle mass and strength have been found to have occurred when steroids are taken in conjunction with a programme of muscle-building exercise and high-protein diet, there is medical consensus on adverse effects caused by large doses and prolonged or repeated use. An added risk is the availability of anabolic steroids on the black market where the make-up or origin is unknown.

## Doping control tests
Doping control tests were introduced to competitions in the 1960s to reduce unfair competition and to deter cheating. Penalties for competitors found to have abused drugs have been devised to exclude the abusers from competing in sport. In the UK testing has been extended to cover the out-of-competition periods. The UK Sports Council operates an independent doping-control programme for British sportsmen and women.

## Is it worth it?
Sportsmen and women are under great pressure to perform well, and may turn to drugs to improve their performance, often assuming that everyone else is taking drugs. However, the use of anabolic steroids can result in serious damage to health and can possibly lead to premature death.

When steroid abuse is detected by a drugs test, the competitor abusing drugs faces the possibility of being excluded from competition for a period of time, even for life.

It should be remembered that there are other substances which also have anabolic effects which are not steroids but which none-the-less are banned.

• The above is an extract from an information sheet produced by the UK Sports Council. See page 41 for address details.

*© The UK Sports Council*
*August 1993*

# Cheats prosper from soft pedalling on hard drugs

**Duncan Mackay says that when athletics puts money before morals, it gives dopers a green light**

Tony Blair's election campaign slogan of 'tough on crime, tough on the causes of crime' would probably go down like a lead balloon in Lausanne, where the message emanating from the office of the most powerful man in sport is exactly the opposite.

When Juan Antonio Samaranch, the president of the International Olympic Committee, welcomes the world's leading anti-doping researchers to a meeting in the pretty Swiss city on the banks of Lake Geneva tomorrow he will tell them how important it is that they find a reliable test for the banned drugs and hormones that most baffle them.

He will then leave the room and call Primo Nebiolo, the president of the International Amateur Athletic Federation, to remind him how important it is that the IAAF cut the maximum length of their drug bans from four years to two.

Nebiolo will not take much persuading, but should he need a nudge, Samaranch will tell him that the corporate sponsors who bankroll their organisations will quickly be driven away if sport is continually rocked by drug scandals. It's a mixed message that will not be lost on the drug cheats. They have been winning the battle for years, now they know they are close to winning the war.

Last month the IAAF allowed eight countries, including Germany, to abandon the four-year ban because of legal problems. Under German law, the national federation cannot suspend any athlete who fails a drugs test for more than two years because it constitutes restraint of trade. That's a bit like saying a burglar can't serve more than two years in jail because otherwise he won't be able to do his job properly.

In 1995 the IAAF voted against a proposal to cut the four-year ban, introduced following the backlash of the Ben Johnson scandal, for serious drugs like steroids after the British Athletic Federation's executive chairman Peter Radford gave a stirring performance – the German delegate compared it to a Winston Churchill speech – which convinced the congress it would send the wrong signal to drug cheats. But now the congress in Athens in July will be urged by Nebiolo to ignore the moral aspect and face the practicalities of civil law.

> **'The fact is that punishment doesn't work . . . every time you have a product which can be detected they switch to another'**

'We have to have rules that are enforceable by law,' said Arne Ljungqvist, the head of the IAAF's medical commission. 'The proposal for a minimum of two years has the support of many federations.' What it effectively means is that any athlete who fails a drugs test in Athens will have time to serve a two-year ban and still be eligible to compete in the 2000 Olympic Games in Sydney and cash in on the financial rewards that a gold medal can bring.

Hein Verbruggen, the head of the World Cycling Federation, the UCI, wants to be even softer on the cheats because he believes the traditional 'ban and punish' system has failed.

'The fact is that punishment doesn't work,' he said. 'Every time you have a product which can be detected they switch to another. In a certain way, by putting more and more products on the list, you enhance the belief in doping because guys feel it must help them.'

The UCI have this year pioneered what they call 'health testing' to try to stamp out the use of EPO, a synthetic drug used to treat kidney patients. Before each major race, cyclists are selected for a random blood test and those whose level of red cells is above a certain level – usually a sign that they have been using EPO – will not be allowed to start. But they will not be banned and will be allowed back into the

saddle when their red cell count returns to an acceptable level.

The medical scientists who will meet in Lausanne are trying to develop legally binding tests that distinguish between naturally produced and artificial EPO, human growth hormone and testosterone.

EPO boosts endurance by stimulating production of red blood cells which transport oxygen to working muscles. Excessive levels can thicken blood, resulting in high blood pressure and even heart attacks. Human growth hormone and the male hormone testosterone help to build muscle and enable athletes to train harder and recover faster.

In the continual cat-and-mouse game between drug testers and drug users, the cheats have stayed ahead by finding new methods and products to beat the system. With steroids readily detectable these days, athletes have increasingly turned to human growth hormone in the knowledge they won't be caught. The hormone, known as hGH, can increase lean body mass and strength.

HGH, which can be administered orally or by injection, can be obtained on the black market. There have also been reports of hGH disappearing from hospitals in robberies.

Laboratories in Italy and Sweden have reported promising results so far. While no one is predicting when an EPO test will be ready for use, experts agree it is likely to be before an hGH procedure is implemented.

But there will be an air of depression hanging over the meeting in Lausanne. 'We know that even if we come up with a test for all these substances there will soon be another drug on the market and we have to start all over again,' said one prominent dope-buster who will be attending the conference. 'But the worst thing is that we get the impression the IOC are beginning to resent our work and they would really rather no one got caught so the public thinks everything is hunky-dory.'

© The Observer
April, 1997

# Norway, France, UK wage war on drugs cheats

**By Andrew Warshaw**

Six countries, including France, Norway and Britain, are stepping up the war against drug cheats in sport by signing a revolutionary agreement which, they hope, will reduce the growing number of civil suits brought by banned athletes.

Fed up with what they perceive as lack of progress by the International Olympic Committee and international sports federations, the six countries, who also include Australia, New Zealand and Canada, hope the government-funded accord will help standardise doping procedures and assist out-of-competition testing.

'The lack of responsibility from the sporting community for better scientific back-up is so provoking and alarming that it is difficult to understand,' said Hans B. Skaset, director-general of the Norwegian Ministry of Cultural Affairs, who is heading the Norwegian side of the programme. 'The IOC has been, and still is, in a position to do considerably more than what has actually been initiated.'

Skaset said he hoped a new doping system could be implemented within a year of the accord being signed. Currently, when a competitor is found guilty, he said, the IOC immediately withdraws from the scene and delegates responsibility to national federations 'who in most cases have no interest, knowledge or wish to be left with such an unpleasant responsibility'.

Skaset said athletes snared in major events were the tip of the iceberg. 'Testing in competition has no bearing on the cleanliness of a sport,' he said. 'Unless you are a damn fool, nobody risks being caught while they are competing.'

Although out-of-competition testing has long been conducted by the International Amateur Athletic Federation, each of the six signatories

*It means, for instance, that if Norway wants to test its athletes in Australia, it can ask the French if they want theirs tested too*

of the new accord can carry out testing on behalf of the others. It means, for instance, that if Norway wants to test its athletes in Australia, it can ask the French if they want theirs tested too.

Michele Verroken, head of doping control for the UK Sports Council, said: 'The idea is to declare an international standard. Our research has shown that athletes would welcome an independent body that has no vested interest.'

Verroken said it was crucial to standardise doping procedure in order to avoid the alarming number of legal cases by banned athletes who feel unjustly treated.

'One of the concerns is that there are different standards and procedures in different countries. Athletes are fearful of their careers being badly affected by an irregularity such as a mistake in the sample collection procedures. We want to provide a quality service that reduces legal challenges and in which athletes can be confident.'

An IOC spokeswoman said: 'All I can say is that we are co-operating closely with these six countries.'

© The European
September, 1997

# Message in a bottle

**Tony Ward believes the war on dope cheats is now futile, and that money should be spent on education rather than a costly witch-hunt**

As they scuttle around the country zealously trying to ensnare sporting drug-takers by making athletes instantly urinate into bottles, it probably does not occur to UK Sports Council sampling officers that they are close to infringing human rights. They are on a mission, pursued with religious fervour, to fight the evil of drug abuse. Nor does it occur to anti-drug groups that their evangelism could lead to the financial ruin of both an athlete and a sporting federation, as they battle to the bitter end to establish guilt or innocence. The lessons of the Diane Modahl case have not been learnt.

Half a million pounds has already collectively been spent on the Modahl hearings (not over yet as the case rumbles on through the civil courts) and the British Athletic Federation has probably almost spent that amount over the past five years or so on drug hearings.

The athletics hierarchy's attitude to the Modahl case is: well, she got off didn't she, sometimes accompanied by a winked innuendo. That she had to spend well over a quarter of a million pounds in clearing her name seems of little consequence to most people in the sport. It was her choice, they say. It was, however, a choice dictated by the fact that drug hearings under the athletics federation are, like our court system, adversarial with all the trappings of a court with the accompanying media attention. Surely in any civilised society the hunt for the truth in such a minor matter should rest with the sport concerned. Surely it is not up to the athletes to prove themselves innocent?

---

*There must be a more even balance of funding between testing on the one hand and fact-finding and education on the other*

---

British athletics has always relished its role as the advocate of draconian deterrence in the fight against drug abuse. But its zealotry has linked itself in my mind with the Salem witchcraft trials of 1692, brilliantly dramatised by Arthur Miller in his play *The Crucible*. Sport abounds with accusations of drug misuse: a world record performance immediately creates a welter of innuendo. There are those among us who believe that every major athlete is on drugs; while drug misuse does not create the hysteria of Salem it does create hysterical statements that high percentages of athletes are on drugs.

We even have our own Witch-finder General in Sir Arthur Gold, for decades a lone voice against drugs misuse in sport. But after 1988 and the Ben Johnson scandal when it became fashionable to fight drug misuse and to frenetically report it, it was the hard-line attitude of Gold (now 80 years of age and still chairman of the BAF Drug Advisory group) that prevailed.

Out-of-competition testing is taken to limits that challenge basic human rights. A test where an athlete is given no notice of intent is hailed as a triumph that will send a message of fear throughout the sport. And should an athlete claim his statutory

I'M NOT SAYING HE'S ON DRUGS BUT THAT'S THE TWENTIETH TIME HE'S LAPPED US!

5,000 METRES

24-hour notice period he or she immediately comes under suspicion. Unlike all other committees in the sport the drug advisory committee is not elected democratically but is under the patronage of its chairman; ergo, if there is a hard-line chairman there is a hard-line committee. And it has become more secretive to the point of paranoia.

To say the very least this is unhealthy and it spreads fear to the administrators, for in such an atmosphere, where athletes join in a chorus of demanding life bans, where redemption is a dirty word, no one wants to appear soft on drugs. This craven attitude probably led to the half-million pounds being spent on the Modahl hearings.

From the very beginning it was obvious that the reasonable doubt expressed by the appeal panel that cleared her was there. Yet no one spoke up, not even Peter Radford, executive chairman of the BAF, an internationally respected figure in this field. A word from him may well have stopped the proceedings but would also have incurred the wrath of the international body. But surely incurring the wrath of the IAAF was preferable to incurring costs that could have been spent more profitably with the sport in Britain?

In *The Crucible* one of the main accusers, Abigail Williams, stands and hysterically points to certain Salem villagers whom, she says, she witnessed cavorting with the devil. It is a moment of some horror in the play. In 1990 when I watched a performance at the National Theatre I was struck by an eerie coincidence. For just a few days before I had heard a story of Dr Martyn Lucking, a former Commonwealth Games shot put champion, in charge of drug testing at an international meeting in Gateshead, irked by the moans of some athletes present, standing angrily in the centre of the room, pointing one by one to individuals there gathered to ritually urinate, shouting that they had to prove themselves innocent of drug misuse before he would believe otherwise.

It was Dr Lucking who chaired the hearing that found Modahl guilty. The rest of the panel was composed of the members of the drugs com-

mittee. Later the independent appeal panel gave her the benefit of the doubt over probable degradation of the sample. The British Athletic Federation quietly changed its rule on the composition of future drug panels ensuring that it would ' . . . not include a member of the BAF Drug Advisory Committee'.

Arthur Miller wrote that in Salem and in the USA in the fifties at the time of the Senator McCarthy hearings 'the repressions of order were heavier than seemed warranted by the dangers against which the order was organised'. I believe that in drug testing, especially in athletics, we have reached that state. Compared with other individual competitive sports like golf and tennis, athletics is still naïve. It is noticeable that these two sports are far more circumspect in their testing pro-grammes than track and field, realising that an injudicious result could lead to massive damages for restraint of trade. Athletics is the only sport where such huge sums are being expended on hearings and appeals but very little indeed on education against drug misuse.

Because many countries have much less will and finance to undertake random drug testing and the IAAF programme is stretched, athletes can and do escape detection, the dilemma for sport is that nobody knows the extent of the problem. The anti-drug zealots believe it is widespread, the British test results would indicate it is minuscule. As the former opinion holds sway the irregularity increases.

There must be a more even balance of funding between testing on the one hand and fact-finding and education on the other.

Sport must have moderation and understanding in its fight against drug misuse, must study why people go down the path of steroid misuse and learn to give redemption and counselling more willingly to those who have erred.

• Tony Ward, former BAF public relations officer, is author of the athletics best-seller *The Golden Decade*.

# *Olympic chief calls for drug leniency*

### By Neil Wilson

The most senior Olympic medical expert was attacked yesterday for suggesting that four-year bans for drug-takers should be halved. Prince Alexandre de Merode, president of the International Olympic Committee's medical commission, came out against the life bans of weightlifting and the four-year bans of athletics and swimming in the IOC's own magazine.

De Merode, who chairs the Olympic committee which determines drug cases at Olympic Games, said: 'The level of sanctions is, in my opinion, excessive. In some aspects it is completely obsolete.' He added that what was fine in the days when all Olympic competitors were amateurs was not realistic in an age when most were professionals. 'If we want to be realistic today it is necessary to review sanctions.'

But de Merode's view met with a withering response from the British Athletic Federation, which led the defence of four-year bans within the IAAF last year. 'He is completely out of touch,' said spokesman Tony Ward.

'If you ask the top athletes in Britain they say they want life bans. Linford Christie has often repeated that. And the national federations were overwhelmingly in favour when the IAAF last voted on it last year.'

# World scientists seek to beat drug cheats

## Andrew Warshaw on a crucial think-tank in Switzerland

The biggest single gathering of sports medicine scientists is set to convene in Switzerland to hammer out a way of detecting EPO, the so-called wonder drug that is believed to be causing widespread cheating throughout sport.

Some 30 anti-doping experts from across the world will spend two days at International Olympic Committee headquarters in Lausanne on 22 and 23 April to establish how far they have come in the war against the drug cheats and where to go from here.

'This is a very important meeting, the first time that we have brought together so many top-level scientists working together,' said Spain's Professor Jordi Segura, who heads the International Olympic Committee's (IOC) anti-doping laboratory in Barcelona. 'We believe that very soon we will have the tools to detect EPO and human growth hormones clearly.'

Panellists will include Prince Alexandre de Merode, president of the IOC medical commission, and Professor Arne Ljungqvist, head of

the equivalent body at the International Amateur Athletic Association. EPO enables an athlete to enhance his or her performance by raising the number of red blood cells, which carry oxygen.

Segura, who was responsible for anti-doping control at the Barcelona Olympics, said a lot of misinfor-

---

*'We believe that very soon we will have the tools to detect EPO and human growth hormones clearly.'*

---

mation had been circulated about the use of EPO which is believed to be particularly prevalent in athletics, Nordic skiing and professional cycling.

'The main goal is to have direct information from the people who really know about the subject,' said Segura.

'There are some burning issues to be discussed.'

Segura said that in addition to EPO, the meeting would concentrate on human growth hormones and steroids.

He rejected the suggestion that science would never catch up with the cheats.

Cycling has already waged war on EPO, an artificially produced hormone that is rapidly replacing the more easily detectable anabolic steroids, by enforcing blood tests on riders after a succession of drug-related deaths.

Any rider found to contain a particularly high level of haemoglobin can be barred from competing.

© *The European*
*April, 1997*

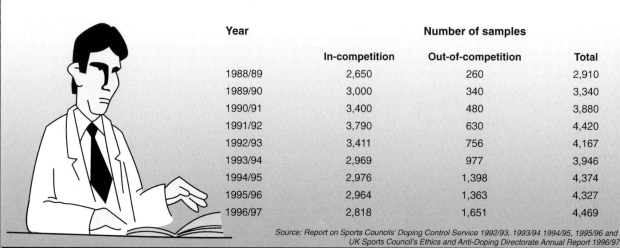

## Testing programme

**Systematic testing in the UK was introduced by the Sports Council (now the UK Sports Council) in 1988. The number of tests annually has continued to rise each year**

| Year | In-competition | Out-of-competition | Total |
|------|---------------|--------------------|-------|
| 1988/89 | 2,650 | 260 | 2,910 |
| 1989/90 | 3,000 | 340 | 3,340 |
| 1990/91 | 3,400 | 480 | 3,880 |
| 1991/92 | 3,790 | 630 | 4,420 |
| 1992/93 | 3,411 | 756 | 4,167 |
| 1993/94 | 2,969 | 977 | 3,946 |
| 1994/95 | 2,976 | 1,398 | 4,374 |
| 1995/96 | 2,964 | 1,363 | 4,327 |
| 1996/97 | 2,818 | 1,651 | 4,469 |

*Source: Report on Sports Councils' Doping Control Service 1992/93, 1993/94 1994/95, 1995/96 and UK Sports Council's Ethics and Anti-Doping Directorate Annual Report 1996/97*

# The professional's feedback

## Players and managers speak out

*The England team coach says . . .*
'Drugs and football just don't go together. Drugs are dangerous and can ruin a person's life by bringing misery, illness, and unhappiness. Football is about fun, pleasure, sportsmanship and achieving something from your own natural effort and ability.'

'It's great to be at the top in football but the fun is in playing your best at any level. To do that you have to be fit and healthy and that means looking at the way you live and the things you do that will help you become the best you can be.'

*Darren Anderton*

'Would you like to be captain of England? It was my dream come true. You'll have to practise, train and always aim to do your best to achieve your best. Your health is the thing you need most to reach the top in football. So for everything you do ask the question: "Will this improve my health or will it only end up making me unfit for football?"'

**David Platt**

'Obviously there is a social problem more than a sports problem with regard to drugs and because they're young men that are in the public eye people are going to latch on to them, and, I would guess, maybe offer them substances that are going to be very very harmful: first and foremost to their health but secondly to their career.'

*Ron Atkinson*

'You just don't need it. Certainly I've never had any and no one I've been associated with has taken drugs. It's never even entered my mind to take it. I think that if you want to be a good footballer and go all the way to the top, then I think the answer is

don't go anywhere near them and don't even touch them.'

*Alan Shearer*

'If you play for one club, another person may support the other club, not like you, not like your club. So they want to see you fail. They want to bring you down in any way they can. So not even just being offered drugs, just even associating yourself with people who may take drugs or be in the situation or be in a club where drugs are used is not on at all.'

*John Barnes*

'It is every schoolboy's dream to be a professional footballer. 99% of them never get the chance. If you've got the chance, don't throw it away.'

*Garth Crooks*

'Don't even think about it. It's as simple as that. In every generation of life there seems to be some problem that's beset youngsters and more and more now it's drugs. Don't even think

about it: forget your career, it's your life you'll ruin.'

*Joe Royle*

'If so-called mates are on drugs they cannot be called mates because they couldn't be mates in the first place to be taking drugs so I would advise friends of mine anyway not to be taking drugs.'

*Andy Cole*

'Being fit and being healthy are equally important to natural ability if you want to achieve your potential as a footballer. That means doing those things that help you to be fit and healthy and avoiding those things that don't. Doing drugs will not make you fit for football, and for life.'

*Terry Venables*
*Ex-England team coach*
• The above is an extract from *Fit for Football*, produced by the Football Association. See page 41 for address details.    ©*Football Association*

# Skin up and you're off!

## Drugs and football

### 'Wizard' of the Rovers

Young footballers are under more pressure today than ever before. Years ago footballers were paid peanuts to play with a ball that was as heavy as a lead pumpkin. They wore flat caps, heavy boots and shorts down to their ankles. At half-time many of them would have a glass of ale, smoke a fag or light a pipe. They might have been footballers but not as we know them today.

### They think it's all over . . . it is now!

If you want to see how the game has changed just look at the video of the 1966 World Cup and compare the pace of that game to today. The 1966 World Cup players were pedestrians compared to the footballing athletes of the late 1990s. To be successful and compete at the top in football today you simply cannot afford to be impressed by the stories of players who stayed up all night drinking and smoking with long-legged girls and still turned up on a Saturday morning and played when the game was much slower.

### Kicking for a living (Not living for kicks)

Today's young footballers are top-class athletes that are worshipped like pop stars. But there is a big difference between pop stars and footballers. Pop stars work at night and can sleep all day. They are expected to work and party all night and sleep most of the day. Footballers have to train hard most days and actually play games on other days.

### It's tough at the top, kid!

It is very tempting for footballers to live the life of a pop star. But this is simply not on for an athlete. You cannot drink and take drugs all night and fall out of a night-club and into bed with Miss World at 4 a.m. and be ready for training at 9 a.m. Forget all the jokes about the hard-drinking superstar footballer being a real 'Lad's lad' and remember the pathetic drunk whose life has been plagued by one set of hangovers and hangers-on after another. They have few real friends but loads of hangers-on who want to spend their money and have a laugh at their expense. All of these so-called friends are in short supply when our star is checking into yet another treatment clinic.

### Just say . . .

In today's society drug and drink problems are everywhere including professional football. But the game is determined to stamp these problems out. So next time some creep says: 'Go on, have another drink or have one of these tablets'

Go tell them to shove their drink and drugs where the sun never shines. These people may as well be saying: 'Go on ruin your career end up on the dole it's just a laugh!'

Young footballers are paid very good money to play football and they are in a much better position to refuse offers of drugs than many other young people. When offered drugs even by a good friend who you might not want to offend you can simply say: 'Thanks but I could be tested next week and that could be me finished!'

They would have to be a real nasty piece of work if they didn't say: 'Oh, right, yeah, I forgot about that. No problem!'

### Easy money

Young footballers need to be careful about the type of friends they choose. Wherever there is money and success you will find a whole range of shady people just waiting to pounce on successful young people (including footballers). They will often have some great money-making scheme like setting up a new night-club or car showroom. Be very careful because a lot of these people are gangsters. But, whether real or plastic they will almost always be involved with drugs and/or drug dealers.

Illegal drugs are one of the biggest earners for dodgy and shady people of all kinds. Young footballers have money. Drug dealers know this and may want you to become one of their best customers or they may want to borrow some of your money to finance their next purchase of drugs. You know the kind of thing: 'Listen mate, just lend me £5,000 till Sunday

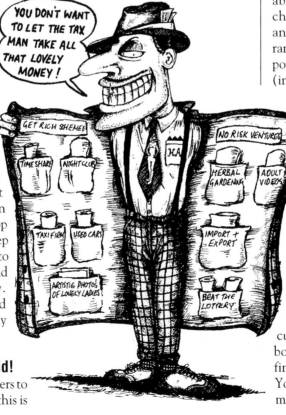

YOU DON'T WANT TO LET THE TAX MAN TAKE ALL THAT LOVELY MONEY!

GET RICH SHEMES
TIME SHARE
NIGHTCLUB
TAXI FIRM
USED CARS
ARTISTIC PHOTO'S OF LOVELY LADIES
NO RISK VENTURES
HERBAL GARDENING
ADULT VIDEOS
IMPORT + EXPORT
BEAT THE LOTTERY

and I'll give you £6,000 back – it's the easiest money you'll ever make!' But it isn't! This is often the first step into the world of drugs, heavy drinking and crime.

### Gambling with your career

Another place where young footballers and Mister Dodgy and Shady often meet is at the bookmaker, the race track, the dog track or the casino. Over the years many famous footballing careers have been blown because of gambling debts. There is nothing wrong with having the odd bet. But remember, gambling attracts the kind of people who would suck you in and spit you out as soon as look at you. They don't give two wags of a horse's tail who you play for or what your career means to you. To them you are a meal ticket. In this world drugs are never far away. So be on your guard when having a flutter.

### Everybody is at it . . .

In the UK currently there are many different drug scenes. There are people who are heavily addicted to drugs like heroin ('brown', 'smack'), cocaine ('charlie', 'coke', 'crack', 'stone', 'rocks') and amphetamines ('whiz', 'speed', 'billy'). Many of these people will be injecting their drugs of addiction. These people are most people's idea of what a proper 'junkie' is.

But there are other people who just use drugs like ecstasy ('E's), LSD ('trips', 'acid'), cocaine, amphetamine and cannabis ('weed', 'draw', 'puff') at weekends or on an occasional basis. These people will not be injecting their drugs. Very few of these people would come across as most people's idea of what a proper 'junkie' is. 'Recreational' or 'social' drugs users can be found everywhere and in every walk of life. For most of these people their drug use will remain recreational and without major problems.

### . . . but you're different

We don't want to make you paranoid (honestly!) but it can be a nasty and brutal world out there and drugs are right at the centre of operations. In fact if

current trends continue the people who do not use drugs will be in the minority. Non-drug users will be different. But, young footballers are already different.

Many young people do not have your talent and do not have any idea of where they are going in life. You do know what you want to be – a successful footballer. If you want to achieve this ambition you'd better get one thing clear. There is no room for illegal drugs of any kind. Even many of the legal drugs (such as those taken as cough medicines and cold cures) contain substances that could see you lose your career.

Never, ever take any medicine without checking it out first with your club doctor or physiotherapist.

### Know the score

'Recreational' drug use may not cause major problems for most young people. However, this is not true of professional footballers. Just one puff on a cannabis 'joint' can lead to a positive urine sample and may end your career. Cannabis can stay in the blood stream for up to eight weeks. Think about that fact before you have a quick blast of weed, a line of coke or whiz or an 'E'. You are playing

for some really high stakes here and it's just not worth it, because you might be the one that gets caught.

Remember: a drug like cannabis can stay in the blood stream for up to eight weeks.

### The early, long . . . long bath

Drug addicts and recreational drug users who are also footballers run the risk of being found guilty of using illegal 'social' drugs. Others will be running the risk of being found guilty of using legal medicines that contain substances that are banned because they are said to have the ability to improve a footballer's performance. These drugs (including the steroids) are called 'performance-enhancing'. The message for professional footballer's is clear, you can't take anything into your body unless you are sure it won't get you into trouble for being a 'social' drug or a 'performance-enhancing' drug. Be careful out there. You have got more to lose than almost any other young person you might have grown up with. Do not let it all get wasted for the sake of a quick 'buzz'.

### Pushing to the limit

The last word must go to the parents and families of would-be professional footballers. Some of the people who have resorted to drugs have done so to escape from the intense pressure that is placed upon them to succeed by parents who push too hard. If a young person has the ability and the desire to become a professional footballer all they need is encouragement and support. They do not need to be subjected to intense pressure from pushy parents who, perhaps with the best intentions, make life unbearable for the young footballer. For these young players, football soon becomes a chore, something they have to do, not something they want to do. One of the saddest cases we have dealt with was a young person who found comfort in heroin as a way of escaping from the pressures to succeed placed on him by his parents.

© *Reproduced with kind permission from the Football Association*

# The race against drugs

## Does anyone care if the athletes all cheat? By Ian Thomsen

It was a bit like asking the Pope about premarital sex, but I posed the question anyway. Could he imagine the day when performance-enhancing drugs will be legalized for athletes?

'No, I don't think so,' said Dr Arne Ljungqvist, the 66-year-old Swede who oversees track and field's ever-controversial war on drugs. 'Being a doctor this is for me very easy. Medical ethics tell me that drugs are intended for the prevention and cure of disease. They are not to be taken by healthy people. Drugs are not intended for this use. It is fundamentally wrong.'

Especially when the drugs themselves are harmful.

He was speaking shortly after the announcement on Thursday of three positive drug tests by athletes at the 6th IAAF World Championships. Dr Ljungqvist, chairman of the IAAF medical and doping commissions, held up these results as proof that drug users in track and field were being apprehended.

Yes, but the illegal samples had been captured from athletes of little public influence. Since the 1988 Olympics, few renowned runners have tested positive.

I felt almost guilty raising innuendo with Dr Ljungqvist, but there is a feeling that the corporations who sponsor the main Olympic sports have no interest in having their relationship besmirched by positive drug tests. We have all seen how quickly such sponsors drop stars who become involved in scandal.

So, it stands to reason, they would have no interest in sponsoring the Olympics if the athletes most responsible for promoting soft drinks and colour film were turning out to be drug cheats on a regular basis.

Dr Ljungqvist said he had heard rumours of athletes whose positive drug tests had been covered up, supposedly to protect the sport.

'I hate these types of unsupported rumours,' he said. 'Give me the evidence and I will act. I promise you.'

The biggest complication is the public's ambivalence. Fans don't want to hear about drug tests. American football players are bigger and more explosive than ever, but the public has not demanded an improved drug-testing programme. The audience of millions of Americans who have turned gymnastics and figure skating into major sports watch those little girls compete without knowing, or wanting to know, the tortures some of them go through – the growth-stunting, the drugs, as well as the endless, numbing hours of practice.

There have been many acceptable improvements in the science of sports training. But there are the other more secretive means – the steroid injections that resulted in the Ben Johnson scandal nine years ago, for example.

Naturally produced drugs such as human growth hormone or erythropoietin (EPO) are, Dr Ljungqvist admitted, difficult for tests to register at levels that would stand up in court. It is because the courts are

encroaching on the fiefdom of global federations that the IAAF was forced last week to take the backward step of halving penalties for major first-time offences, to a maximum suspension of two years. Repeat offenders will still be banned for life.

The athletes, who make all kinds of physical and emotional sacrifices, are willing to risk the ultimate sacrifice.

'I realise the problem – I think we all do – the incompatibility there is,' Dr Ljungqvist said. He meant the incompatibility between the ambition to achieve new standards of excellence and the standards of morality which should never be violated. Sponsors love the Olympics because Olympians appear to satisfy both sides of the equation. The doctor, however, preferred to discuss only the facts.

'We know in our sport that last year there were 1,745 samples conducted on elite track-and-field athletes around the world, with very few positives,' he said. 'Others claim that because we find a few drug users, our sport is filled with drugs. There is no hard data to support that view.'

But there are clues. Dr Ljungqvist said he has heard talk that some former East German athletes are considering lawsuits against the officials and coaches who supplied them with dangerous performance-enhancing drugs. It is also not beyond reason that someday a famous athlete, a role model of healthy achievements, might fall to the tumours, heart problems and other decay that can accompany the use of hormones or steroids. Just as Rock Hudson's death promoted awareness of AIDS, so we would be forced to pay attention to the destructive pressures of sport. May it never come to that.

© International Herald Tribune
August, 1997

# Games scandal of drug they call Silent Speed

**Olympic tests don't detect new hormone. By Bob Graham in Amsterdam**

A new drug known to athletes as Silent Speed is being widely used by athletes at the Olympic Games, it was claimed last night.

The drug, available on the black market in Holland and Belgium, is not detectable by the doping tests conducted in Atlanta.

It is a human growth hormone known to pharmacists and chemists as STH, or Somatropin Hormone. A Daily Express investigation has revealed the widespread use of STH and other drugs which also avoid detection in Olympic tests.

Dr Michel Karsten, a critic of doping controls used by international sports organisations, said: 'When I look at some of the sportsmen and women standing on the medal podium I smile because I know for a fact they have taken drugs to enhance their performances.'

The Dutch GP admits he has been prescribing drugs and advising top sports stars – including British athletes – about the use of anabolic steroids for the past 20 years. He refuses to name any of his clients, but says the numbers 'run into thousands'.

'At first I counselled them about the dangers,' he said in an exclusive interview. 'Then when they told me they intended to take the drugs whatever I said, I realised I had a medical duty to advise them properly to ensure the risks to their health were minimised.'

> **'We must all realise there is no such thing as fair play. The Games are no longer about ideals. The drug testing is a joke and every athlete and sports federation knows it'**

Now the highly-regarded doctor is trying to persuade the Dutch sports authorities to change their rules to become the first country that 'openly' admits its sports stars take performance-enhancing drugs. 'We must all realise there is no such thing as fair play. The Games are no longer about ideals. The drug testing is a joke and every athlete and sports federation knows it.'

But two Russian medal winners who were disqualified after failing dope tests at Atlanta were yesterday reinstated.

The Court of Arbitration for Sport said it accepted the appeal by swimmer Andrei Korneyev and wrestler Zafar Guliyev, who tested positive for a stimulant. They will get their medals back.

Meanwhile, two British Olympic athletes last night resorted to selling items from their official Great Britain team kit at a street stall to raise cash.

Divers Robert Morgan and Tony Ali, who competed in the Olympic pool, are returning home to a jobless future in Sheffield. Last night, one British team official said: 'This highlights the poor prospects most of our sportsmen and women are facing.'

*© The Daily Express*
*August, 1996*

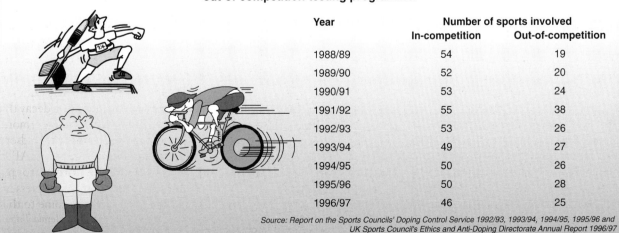

## Testing programme by sport

**The number of sports involved in the drug-testing programme has remained fairly constant since June, 1988. However, there has been an increase in those sports covered by the out-of-competition testing programme.**

| Year | Number of sports involved | |
|------|---------------|-------------------|
| | In-competition | Out-of-competition |
| 1988/89 | 54 | 19 |
| 1989/90 | 52 | 20 |
| 1990/91 | 53 | 24 |
| 1991/92 | 55 | 38 |
| 1992/93 | 53 | 26 |
| 1993/94 | 49 | 27 |
| 1994/95 | 50 | 26 |
| 1995/96 | 50 | 28 |
| 1996/97 | 46 | 25 |

*Source: Report on the Sports Councils' Doping Control Service 1992/93, 1993/94, 1994/95, 1995/96 and UK Sports Council's Ethics and Anti-Doping Directorate Annual Report 1996/97*

# The non-medical social use of drugs

**How much of a risk? By Harry Shapiro**

Mention drugs and sport together and most people will think no further than anabolic steroids and Ben Johnson. But as ordinary citizens, many young people involved in sport at whatever level will also be engaged in the non-medical use of drugs – sometimes to try and improve performance, but mainly for social reasons.

A recent audit of drug statistics and surveys in Britain conducted by the Institute for the Study of Drug Dependence (ISDD) showed clearly that drug use among young people is at record levels; by the age of twenty up to a third have tried illegal drugs or solvents, a quarter (over two million) would have tried cannabis and between 5 and 10% would have tried a whole range of other substances; in particular LSD and Ecstasy. A similar survey five years ago would have shown perhaps a 1-2% incidence of LSD use among teenagers while Ecstasy just wasn't around.

What this amounts to is a situation where drugs have come in from the fringes of society, no longer resident in the subculture or a rallying point for counterculture, but on the way to becoming simply another aspect of mainstream popular culture.

There is some comfort to be taken from the fact that despite the high levels of experimentation with many different drugs, young people remain largely resistant to drugs such as heroin and cocaine – plus the idea of injecting any drug – and very few become drug-dependent. But clearly, anti-drug campaigns encouraging young people to 'Just Say No' to drugs have failed to curb experimentation and perhaps were always likely to be unsuccessful. Attempting to change behaviour patterns with national campaigns of this sort has a poor track record of success. Young people will inevitably try out activities which often generate adult disapproval – drinking, smoking, sex, riding fast motorbikes and so on – why should they listen any harder when lectured about drug use?

A more realistic way forward is to acknowledge that experimentation will happen and to limit the potential damage which drugs can cause by arming young people with the accurate and non-sensational information they often seek themselves to make their own decisions about using drugs. Drug information should also be relevant and credible. If, for example, you tell young people that smoking cannabis leads to heroin addiction and they know full well from personal experience that this just isn't true – then you have lost their respect.

Drug effects are determined by a whole range of factors; the interaction of drug and body chemistry; what the user expects and wants from the experience; the surroundings in which the drug is taken and social and cultural beliefs about the drug among family, friends, and society at large. Thus it can be very misleading to state as the media often does that 'drug x always causes effect y'.

But what are the risks involved? The vast majority of people who use drugs come to no harm. But there are serious risks, some of which apply to all or most drugs. Each drug has its

---

*The vast majority of people who use drugs come to no harm. But there are serious risks, some of which apply to all or most drugs*

---

own array of potential risks and it should not be assumed that the extent to which a drug is legally restricted is much of a guide as to how harmful it can be – witness the damage caused by excessive smoking and drinking.

## Overdoing it

This applies to drugs in two different ways. First taking too much in one go risks the experience getting out of control, causing distress or even overdose. Secondly, anybody taking frequent high doses of a mood-altering drug over a lengthy period is likely to distort their perception of and response to their environment; friends can become restricted to those who use drugs and there can be all kinds of attendant legal, financial, employment and health problems from a life which revolves around drug use. The drugs most likely to cause these kinds of disruptions over the long term would be heroin, cocaine and alcohol.

## Wrong time, wrong place

Even in moderate doses most drugs (except the stimulants) impair motor control, reaction time and the ability to maintain attention – effects which can last several hours. No matter how the person feels – driving, operating machinery, or even crossing the road can be dangerous. Many deaths from solvent misuse have happened because of accidents caused through intoxication. The recent spate of Ecstasy deaths has been linked to the combination of drug effect and heatstroke brought on by dancing for hours on end in crowded dance venues. Also, many drugs amplify mood. For example, anybody feeling depressed, or angry, may become more so by drinking, or increase their chances of a bad LSD trip if they were depressed or anxious beforehand.

## Individual differences

As in life generally, so with drugs – there is no such thing as a 'normal' person. Effects vary according to weight and gender. Some people develop a toxic reaction to a single cup of coffee; might experience pain from smoking cannabis if they suffer from angina, or could have a latent mental condition tripped by taking LSD. Anybody with a heart condition taking stimulants such as amphetamine, Ecstasy or cocaine is clearly putting themselves at risk.

## Adulteration and mistaken identity

In the world of illegal drugs, there is no quality control; many drugs will be adulterated with other drugs or inert substances to make up their weight. Users will have no idea what they are buying, how strong it is, or how much to take.

## Doubling up

The most dangerous form of 'doubling up' is the use of two or more depressant drugs such as alcohol, opiates (e.g. heroin) or tranquillisers. A safe dose of one depressant drug can easily become an overdose with the addition of another.

## Injection

Easily the most dangerous way to take drugs – steroids are often used in this way. The main dangers are overdose (all the drug enters the body at once); infection from non-sterile injecting methods (including hepatitis and HIV) and abscesses, gangrene, blood poisoning and other conditions associated with poor injecting techniques or by injecting drugs never meant for this purpose, such as crushed pills. These are potentially the most serious risks of using drugs. Readers wanting more detailed information about various aspects of drug misuse, including drugs in sport, should contact the Information Officer at ISDD on 0171-430 1993.

## Health risks of drugs

The following are some of the potential health risks of using specific drugs. They are not inevitable outcomes of drug use nor are they necessarily part of a user's common experience.

### Alcohol
Impaired mental and physical performance; overdose (especially if taken with another depressant drug); physical and psychological dependence; potentially dangerous withdrawal syndrome (delirium tremens); brain, liver and kidney damage.

### Amphetamines
High doses causing anxiety, nervousness, insomnia. Regular high doses causing cardiovascular problems, ill health due to lack of proper food (stimulants suppress appetite); temporary paranoid psychosis; physical and psychological dependence; withdrawal not life-threatening, but feelings of hunger, fatigue and often deep depression.

### Cannabis
Impaired mental and physical performance; respiratory problems; psychological dependence.

### Cocaine and crack
As for amphetamines, but more acute. Damage to nasal membranes through sniffing; respiratory problems through smoking crack.

### Ecstasy
As for amphetamines in high doses; idiosyncratic toxic reaction with symptoms similar to heatstrokes; cardiovascular problems; liver damage; psychological dependence.

### Heroin
Overdose (especially if taken with another depressant drug); physical and psychological dependence; gastro-intestinal problems; withdrawal not life-threatening, but symptoms unpleasant for up to a week.

### LSD and 'magic' mushrooms
Hallucinations and visions can be unpleasant causing anxiety and panic; impaired physical and mental performance.

### Solvents
Impaired mental and physical performance; toxic reactions causing respiratory and/or cardiovascular collapse; psychological dependence.

### Tobacco
Respiratory and cardiovascular problems; psychological dependence.

### Tranquillisers
Impaired physical and mental performance; overdose (especially if taken with other depressant drugs); physical and psychological dependence; withdrawal symptoms unpleasant and long lasting.

### Injecting any drug
Infection caused by using unsterile injecting equipment (hepatitis, HIV); blood poisoning, abscesses, gangrene, thrombosis; overdose.

## Summary

1. Non-medical drug use among young people is at record levels.
2. Simply telling young people not to take drugs has little effect.
3. Equally ineffective is trying to scare young people about the dangers of drug use if this information doesn't match with personal experience.
4. Most young people who try drugs will come to no harm at all.
5. Many young people who use drugs are keen to know how they can protect themselves from harm.
6. It is a realistic not defeatist approach to acknowledge drug use by young people and help them to make their own decisions about drugs.
7. Information should be accurate, credible and relevant to their situation.
8. The legality of a drug is no indication of how harmful it might be.
9. A whole plethora of medical and environmental factors will determine how drugs affect any individual.
10. All drugs carry an element of risk. But some ways of using drugs such as injecting any drug or taking it in an unsafe situation (e.g. sniffing solvents in a derelict building) are far more dangerous than others.

• The above article first appeared in *Coaching Focus* No. 23 and is reproduced by kind permission of the NCF. See page 41 for address details.
© *National Coaching Foundation (NCF) Summer 1993*

# Bromantan is Russians' 'rocket fuel'

**Banned performance-enhancing drugs are becoming more sophisticated. Pat Butcher examines their history**

New Olympics, new drug! The race between the dope takers and the dope testers continues apace. Seoul was stanozolol, Barcelona was clenbuterol, Atlanta it seems was bromantan. The progression is impressive. Stanozolol was, if not the dark ages of drug-taking, then a fairly humble anabolic steroid.

Clenbuterol was rather more sophisticated, in that it was used as a masking agent for other 'harder' drugs. Bromantan has been described here by the Olympic authorities as a 'designer' drug.

Bromantan, which combines the properties of steroid, stimulant and masking agent – effectively the Grand Slam in doping terms – was developed by the Russian national institutes for pharmacology, and has allegedly been used by the Russian army and by astronauts. It is also serving as 'rocket fuel' for Russian and other East European competitors here.

The Russians take full responsibility for the drug, but claim that since it is not on the International Olympic Committee banned lists, then no action should be taken against those competitors here who have tested positive for it.

The IOC do not agree. What started as a trickle in the swimming pool threatens to turn into a flood. First, breaststroker Andrei Korneyev was stripped of his bronze medal over it. Then backstroker Nina Zhuvaniskya tested positive followed quickly by the Greco-Roman wrestler, Zafar Guleyev, who also forfeited his bronze medal. The Lithuanian cyclist Rita Razmaite was suspended, along with a Russian coach and a Belarussian doctor, and finally (thus far) a fourth Russian, Marina Trandekova, who finished fifth in the women's 100 metres, was disqualified. The Russians are appealing over all these and have taken their case to the new Court of Sports Arbitration, which is sitting in special session here.

The Russian team chief, Anatoly Kolesov, insists that the IOC's medical commission has been notified of the drug. 'We sent them a description of the drug two years ago. We didn't get a reply, so we assumed it was safe. It is intended to protect the body's immune system.'

---

*This century has been awash with performance-enhancing substances in sport. And they are getting increasingly sophisticated*

---

But Dr Patrick Schamasch, the IOC medical director, said: 'As far as I know, we received no information on that issue. But every Olympic delegation knows that the list of banned substances only contains examples. The key word is "related compounds". Doctors know what that means'.

Kolesov implied that this stance would result in more Russians being disqualified.

Since the Russians claimed that they screened all their competitors before coming to Atlanta, that certainly suggests a belief that the drug was safe. But a warning letter from the International Amateur Athletic Federation to the IOC, which has been passed to *The Independent*, puts a different gloss on the matter.

Dated June 13, 1996, the letter provides a potted history of appearances of the drug in urine samples, dating back to the World Cup cross-country skiing in 1994, when there was one case. Further cases, almost always involving ex-Soviet competitors, in sports as diverse as swimming, figure skating and Nordic Games, are given for the intervening period, from laboratories as far afield as Montreal, Lausanne, Tokyo, and Huddinge in Sweden.

The gist of the IAAF letter is that bromantan has been specifically developed not only to combine the properties of steroid and stimulant, but also to confound any testing system.

Indeed, Prince Alexandre de Merode, president of the IOC medical commission, admitted after the first positive test that he was not sure that his lab would be able to detect bromantan. But a comparison between models from the Montreal lab and the Atlanta samples had enabled them to do so. 'We hope to bring in full proof testing procedures very shortly,' he said.

What the affair underlines, however, is that this is a race which no one can win. Drug-taking in sports did not begin with Ben Johnson, and it will not end in Atlanta. It has existed since the Ancient Olympic Games, although it was not recognised that the sheep's testicles devoured by the wrestlers and boxers were rich in testosterone.

But the distance runners and walkers of a century ago knowingly took strychnine. This century has been awash with performance-enhancing substances in sport. And they are getting increasingly sophisticated. It now seems to be so firmly embedded in the psyche of competitors (and some administrators), and the line between medical back-up and dope-taking is so fine, that it has all become an integral part of competition tactics.

© *The Independent*
*August, 1997*

# Doping in sport

## Information from the UK Sports Council

Drugs and other substances are used by some sportsmen and women to try to do better at sport. The governing bodies of Sport, helped by the UK Sports Council, have introduced measures to make sportsmen and women aware of the dangerous side-effects of misusing drugs and to try and stop any unfair advantage which might be gained by misusing them. These measures are called doping control.

A list of banned drugs has been drawn up by the International Olympic Committee (IOC) which most governing bodies of sport adopt. Breaking the doping control rules is, in a sense, no different from breaking other rules (offside, obstruction, etc.) as you are cheating against your fellow competitors when you break these rules. You are also cheating yourself and could be putting your health at risk by misusing drugs. As a competitor you should check with the governing body to confirm which substances are banned in your sport.

This article outlines the different types of banned drugs, explains what they are, why they can be dangerous and gives examples. The classes of banned drugs are listed below:

*Doping classes:*
Stimulants
Narcotic analgesics
Anabolic agents
Diuretics
Peptide hormones & analogues
Beta-blockers (subject to restriction in certain sports)

*Doping methods:*
Blood doping,
including Erythropoietin (EPO), pharmacological, chemical and physical manipulation
*Remember*: Using banned substances to try to get better at sport can be dangerous. It is also cheating against yourself and your fellow competitors.

## What are stimulants?

Stimulants include various drugs which act on the brain. Competitors may use stimulants to reduce tiredness, to increase alertness, competitiveness and aggression. They are banned because they stimulate the body mentally and physically which may give a competitor an unfair advantage. In addition they produce harmful side-effects.

Competitors have died through misusing stimulants as they make it difficult for the body to cool down, especially when a competitor has been exercising for long periods of time. If the body overheats and is unable to cool down, it dehydrates and blood circulation decreases. The heart and other organs will stop working normally. This can be fatal.

*What harm could stimulants cause?*
Misusing stimulants could cause:
- a rise in blood pressure and body temperature
- increased and irregular heart beat
- aggressiveness and anxiety
- loss of appetite
- addiction

*Examples of stimulant substances*
Amphetamine
Caffeine*
Cocaine
Diethylpropion
Ephedrine*
Phentermine
Phenylpropanalamine*
Strychnine
*Beware – these substances may be found in low doses in cough and cold medications.

If a competitor is found to be using a stimulant, it may be regarded as a doping offence.

## What are narcotic analgesics?

Narcotic analgesics are painkillers. They act on the brain to reduce the amount of pain felt from injury or illness and in medicine they have an important use. However, competitors may use them to offset or deaden pain, to mask injuries and to increase their pain limit. Narcotic analgesics are banned because they are extremely addictive and because they make the original injury much worse.

Increasing the pain threshold may lead to further injury or to permanent damage. Narcotic analgesics can cause physical dependence, leading to addiction.

### What harm could narcotic analgesics cause?

Misuse of narcotic analgesics may cause:

- breathing problems
- nausea and vomiting
- loss of concentration, balance and co-ordination
- addiction

### Examples of narcotic analgesic substances:

Methadone
Morphine
Pethidine

Mild analgesics are found in cold and analgesic treatments without prescription, usually in combination with aspirin (allowable) or caffeine (banned). In small doses, as prescribed by your doctor, these substances are not harmful.

However, if a competitor is found to have misused narcotic analgesics, it may be regarded as a doping offence.

## What are anabolic agents?

The anabolic agents class includes anabolic androgenic steroids and beta2 agonists. Androgenic anabolic steroids are a type of hormone known as testosterone. Whilst there are a small number of medical conditions which could be treated with low doses of androgenic anabolic steroids, in sport they are misused to try to make a competitor larger and stronger. For scientific reasons bigger muscles do

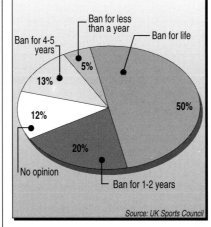

**Athlete's views on sanctions**

The sanctions imposed by different NGB's vary, even within a particular sport where there may be more than one NGB operating. Penalties for first offenders range from 6 months in some sports to a life ban in others. The figures below show that competitors wanted tough penalties for those who were caught for the first time using anabolic steroids.

Ban for 4-5 years — 13%
Ban for less than a year — 5%
Ban for life — 50%
No opinion — 12%
Ban for 1-2 years — 20%

*Source: UK Sports Council*

not necessarily mean extra strength. Androgenic anabolic steroids may increase aggression which may help people train harder. Competitors misuse them in an attempt to increase strength, power and endurance, to build up muscles and to be competitive. In addition to their therapeutic use beta2 agonists may be used for the same reasons. When given systemically (internally) beta2 agonists may have powerful anabolic effects, hence their use is banned. Examples of beta2 agonists are clenbuterol, salbutamol, terbutaline and salmeterol. Only salbutamol and terbutaline are permitted and then only by inhalation (written notification must be given to the relevant medical authority).

Anabolic agents are banned because using them is cheating. In addition there could be harmful effects, particularly when androgenic anabolic steroids are misused for long periods of time and/or in large quantities.

### What harm can androgenic anabolic steroids cause?

Sportsmen and women may be affected by androgenic anabolic steroids in different ways. As hormone substances, they could interfere with the normal hormone balance of the body and increase the risk of liver diseases and premature heart disease. Other harmful effects could include:

In males:
- acne
- increased aggression, sometimes resulting in violent and unacceptable sexual behaviour, in the long term leading to impotence
- kidney damage
- development of breasts
- premature baldness

In females:
- development of male features
- irregular periods
- more hair growth on the face and body
- deepening of the voice
- increased aggression

In adolescents:
- severe acne on the face and body
- stunted growth

### Examples of androgenic anabolic steroid substances:

Boldenone
Mesterolone
Methandienone
Stanozolol
Testosterone
Nandrolone

Competitors found using anabolic agents have broken the doping control rules and have been banned from their sport.

## What are Beta-blockers?

Beta-blockers are drugs used to treat heart disease and to lower blood pressure and heart rate. They could be misused by sports competitors attempting to steady their nerves, and to stop trembling. In particular they could be used in those sports where a competitor needs to keep calm and be relaxed.

### What harm can Beta-blockers cause?

Competitors without a heart problem who misuse Beta-blockers may suffer:
- low blood pressure
- slow heart rate
- tiredness

The heart may stop because it has been slowed down too much.

If Beta-blockers are required by competitors who have a genuine medical need for them a range of effective alternative treatments are available.

*Examples of Beta-blocking drugs:*
Atenolol
Oxprenolol
Propranolol

Beta-blockers are prohibited in sports where physical activity is of little or no importance. Competitors who misuse Beta-blockers and are caught by a drug test could be banned or suspended by their governing body (refer to the regulations of international sports federations).

## What are diuretics?

Diuretics are drugs which help to remove fluids from the body. They can be used medically to treat diseases of the heart, kidney and liver, and for pre-menstrual tension. Diuretics may be misused in sport for two main reasons:

1　to lose weight quickly in sports which have weight categories
2　to increase the rate at which competitors can pass urine, because some believe that this will make it more difficult for the laboratory to detect a banned substance.

Misuse of diuretics has serious health risks, it is also cheating.

### *What harm can diuretics cause?*
Before, during and after exercise, it is essential that sportsmen and women take in a considerable amount of fluid. Competitors who misuse diuretics could suffer from dehydration. If the body has insufficient water to work normally this may cause:

• faintness and dizziness
• muscle cramps
• headaches and nausea

Losing too much water could also cause the kidneys and heart to stop working, which can be fatal.

### *Examples of diuretic substances:*
Bendrofluazide
Frusemide
Hydrochlorothiazide
Triameterine
Spironolactone
If a competitor misuses a diuretic substance, this would be regarded as a doping offence.

## What are peptide hormones and analogues?

Peptide hormones 'carry messages' around the body, to increase growth, influence sexual and general behaviour and to control pain. Analogues are man-made (synthetic) drugs which have similar effects to natural substances. The original and synthetic versions are banned in sport.

Competitors misuse peptide hormones and analogues for various reasons: to stimulate production of naturally occurring (endogenous) steroids, to build up muscles, to mend body tissue and to improve the body's ability to carry oxygen.

### *What harm can misusing peptide hormones and analogues cause?*
Because everyone has hormones in their bodies it is difficult to say specifically how much harm is caused by misusing them.
Chorionic Gonadotrophin:
In men HCG increases production of endogenous steroids and is similar to using testosterone. HCG in small quantities can be found in the urine of pregnant women.

Corticotrophin:
This drug increases the level of endogenous corticosteroids which in turn could cause a feeling of wellbeing. It helps to repair damaged tissues and muscles but if used for long periods of time would cause muscle wasting.

Growth hormone:
In medicine low doses of growth hormones help to treat children with growth problems. However, in sport, adults who attempt to build their muscles using growth hormone risk abnormal growth of the hands, feet and face (Acromegaly) and of the internal organs, e.g. liver. Enlarged organs could cause further health problems if damaged by severe bruising which might occur in a contact sport.

Erythropoietin (EPO):
EPO increases the number of red cells in the blood. However, thickening the blood could be dangerous as it may clot or overload the heart. Increased viscosity of the blood increases the risk of blood clotting and may lead to a stroke.

Competitors found to have misused peptide hormones and analogues have broken the doping control rules and would be punished.

## What is blood doping?

Blood doping is the injection of blood into your body to increase the number of blood cells. Red blood cells carry oxygen to the muscles, giving the body more energy to work. Blood transfusions may be carried out after an operation or illness and should be properly supervised by qualified medical people.

Competitors in endurance activities such as running, cycling, marathons and skiing might use blood doping to increase their energy carrying capacity. Alternatively competitors might use EPO (see peptide hormones and analogues) to create a similar effect.

### *What harm can blood doping cause?*
There are risks involved in the transfusion of blood particularly for those who have no medical need and who already have normal blood levels, these include:

• allergic reactions
• hepatitis or AIDS
• overload of the circulatory system
• blood clots
• kidney damage

Competitors who are involved in blood doping are breaking the doping control rules and if caught would be punished.

*© UK Sports Council*

# Doping control in sport

## Questions & answers

### Why the concern about drugs in sport?

Drugs and other substances are now being taken not for the purposes they were intended, but simply to attempt to enhance performances in sport. It puts the health of the athlete at risk. It can be dangerous. It undermines the foundation of fair competition. It is cheating.

The only legitimate use of drugs in sport is for a medically justified purpose under the supervision of a doctor. Even here medicines should be sought which do not contravene the drug rules and stand no risk of causing harmful effects.

Governing bodies of sport, encouraged and assisted by the UK Sports Council, set up doping control to protect sportsmen and women from dangerous side-effects and to prevent any unfair advantage which might be gained by cheats.

### What is doping control?

It is a system whereby urine samples are collected, tested for banned substances and a disciplinary procedure followed if any are found. The aim is to eradicate the use of drugs to enhance performance.

### Who will be tested?

One cannot know in advance who will be selected for drug testing. Selection is normally made at random on the day of competition or raining session. Some governing bodies of sport specify that the winner in each event plus a number selected at random will be tested.

### How will I know if I am selected?

Sportsmen and women selected for testing will be notified by an authorised official. Those selected will be asked to sign a form to acknowledge that they have been notified and agreed to go to the doping control station no later than a stated time. Usually you can go to the control station straight away.

### Can someone go with me to the control station?

You may be accompanied by an appropriate adult (e.g. your team manager or other official). Usually space is limited so that you cannot bring more than one person with you.

### What happens at the control station?

The control station is a quiet place where the sample of urine can be given and bottled and sealed in the correct way.

You will be asked to identify yourself, the collection procedure will be explained, and you will be asked to:
a) choose a set of two numbered bottles from those available
b) give a sample of urine, under supervision
c) enter on the form any medication you have taken in the past three days
d) check and sign that your sample of urine has been placed in the bottles you chose, that the bottles have been sealed and the numbers recorded correctly, and that you have no complaints concerning the collection procedure.

### What if I cannot produce the required sample?

Don't worry, plenty of drinks will be available and you will be given plenty of time.

### What happens to the samples?

They will be sent to an International Olympic Committee accredited laboratory where they will be analysed.

### What types of drugs are banned?

The main classes are:
a) stimulants
b) narcotic analgesics (strong pain killers)
c) anabolic steroids
d) beta-blockers (restricted for certain sports)
e) diuretics

## What happens if no banned substances are found?

Nothing. A negative result will be reported to the governing body of your sport which requested the testing. The samples will then be destroyed.

## What happens if a banned substance is found?

The governing body will be informed that a particular substance has been found in your sample of urine. The governing body will then notify you.* In general the procedure is then as follows:

(a) you may be suspended from competitions of the governing body while the reason for the presence of the banned substance is considered. For this you* are entitled to:

  i) a second analysis of the urine sample which you* and a representative may observe
  ii) attend* with a representative to present your case.

(b) a decision will then be taken. This may include suspension from competition of the governing body for a period.

(c) You are entitled to appeal against the decision to an authorised body.
* and your parent if you are under 16 years of age.

## How can I be safe?

The only completely safe way is to take no drugs. Many commonly used medications, whether prescribed by a doctor or purchased at a chemist's, may contain banned substances. If medication is required you should check every medication in advance for the presence of a banned substance and do not take any medication you have not checked. Remember this is your responsibility.

Remember your own doctor or chemist may not be aware of the doping regulations for sport so their view on the safety of a medicine may not be correct. A list of examples of banned substances can be obtained from your governing body to show to your doctor. If you have any doubts contact your governing body or the UK Sports Council for further advice.

## What if I need medicines for conditions such as asthma, hay fever

or other complaints, but am still fit enough to take part?

There are usually suitable alternative medicines which do not contain banned substances. Your doctor will be able to advise you in the first instance. But remember it is strongly recommended that the composition of the medicine prescribed is checked against the list of examples of banned substances and with your governing body.

## How long do drugs stay in my system?

This is extremely variable, depending on the drug and the individual. Some drugs can be eliminated rapidly, while for others, traces can remain for several months.

## Can I avoid detection?

No – the sample analysis is extremely sensitive; even trace amounts can be detected and identified.

## Is it worth the risk?

No! It may damage your health and your future in sport. In addition, it could endanger the reputation of your sport in this country and abroad.

## What if I refuse to take the test?

If you are selected for testing but refuse to be tested or do not attend the control station as requested, it is considered as though the urine gave a positive test. The procedure explained opposite is followed. However, as a sample of urine was not given at the time, there is clearly no chance of a second analysis of the sample.

## Couldn't I fill the bottles with someone else's urine?

No – an official will be with you to ensure that the sample is collected in the correct way.

## Why can't I have a list of 'safe' drugs?

No list will be complete. New medications come on the market constantly. The substances banned are subject to change. The safest ways to check that you are not taking a banned substance are given in questions above.

Note: In most circumstances it is illegal to give any drug to a person under 16 without the consent of a parent. Parental consent is also needed for drug testing in this age group.

Remember – you are the best safeguard of your own well-being, now and in the future. Never put your own health at risk.

N.B. This information is for your guidance only. Actual doping procedures may vary slightly according to circumstance.

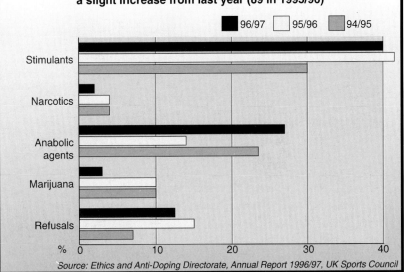

**The 1996/7 testing programme**

During 1996/97 4,469 drug tests were conducted (4,327 in 1995/96) of which nearly 40% were collected out of competition. The testing programme involved 78 national governing bodies and 24 international federations from 47 sports. 98% of the tests conducted in 1996/97 were negative – a small improvement in comparison with the previous year (97.9%). 90 findings were reported to governing bodies in 1996/97 – a slight increase from last year (89 in 1995/96)

96/97  95/96  94/95

Stimulants
Narcotics
Anabolic agents
Marijuana
Refusals

%  0    10    20    30    40

Source: Ethics and Anti-Doping Directorate, Annual Report 1996/97, UK Sports Council

# Drug tests on 9-year-olds

**Young footballers routinely asked for samples in bid to isolate users reports Duncan Campbell, Crime Correspondent**

Footballers as young as nine are being tested for drug use, a police conference heard yesterday. Players aged 12 and 13 are now routinely asked to give samples in an effort to isolate drug use in sport.

There was a call at the conference to decriminalise cautioning for cannabis use and to 'educate the over-30s' in order to demystify drug taking. But the Home Office minister, George Howarth, ruled out any possibility of changing the law on drugs or establishing a royal commission on drug use.

Alan Hodson, administrator of education and medical policy for the Football Association, told the Association of Chief Police Officers' drugs conference at Hinckley, Leicestershire, that his team was now testing, with parents' consent, football players as young as nine.

Mr Hodson said that 491 tests of young players and professional footballers had been carried out last year. There had only been five positive tests – two for cannabis, one for cocaine, one for a cocktail and ecstasy, and one for a medicinal drug. The youngest player to test positive was 17.

Police were not informed of the drug tests, said Mr Hodson. Those tested positive were offered counselling. There was no evidence for the use of performance-enhancing drugs in football.

Gordon Taylor, chief executive of the Professional Footballers' Association, told the conference that while there had been 12 positive tests in the 1994/95 season, this figure had dropped to seven in 1995/96 and fell to five last season.

> **There had only been five positive tests – two for cannabis, one for cocaine, one for a cocktail and ecstasy, and one for a medicinal drug. The youngest player to test positive was 17**

The tests, which cost £230 each, are carried out randomly. Some clubs make specific requests for tests on young players of whom they are suspicious, he said.

Players under 16 were only tested with their parents' approval.

Professional players who refused to take a test were charged with bringing the game into disrepute.

Howard Parker of Manchester University, who had carried out a series of research projects on young people and drugs, told the conference that the UK had the highest proportion of young people taking drugs in Europe. Over half the people in the UK had tried drugs.

Ignorance about drugs came in the over-30 age group, because too many people had an hysterical view about the levels and relative dangers of drug use.

Professor Parker said that he favoured 'a drugs cautioning system for personal use which basically decriminalised possession'.

Mr Howarth told the conference that 'any debate about legislation or decriminalisation detracts from the strong message that drugs destroy lives'. Even a royal commission on cannabis use would send the wrong message.

'I refuse to accept that drugs have become part of growing up,' said Mr Howarth. 'Just one in four young people have taken drugs in the last year, and even fewer, just one in seven, has done so in the last month.'

© *The Guardian*
*June, 1997*

BUT IT'S ONLY SHERBET!

DRUG TESTERS

KenPyne

# Battle hots up in drugs war

## Ban threats for missing two random tests in get-tough move

By Steven Downes in Seville

**A**s she pulled herself out of the San Pablo pool on Thursday night, Michelle Smith's body seemed to shake. It might have been a reaction to fatigue following a third tough final in three days or dismay at her first defeat at these championships.

Just as likely, it was sheer anger at the way Ireland's triple Olympic champion cannot throw off the constant questions about her uniquely rapid improvements.

The following morning, in a temporary office across from the pool, two men sat down for a meeting, determined to find a way to stem the doubts about Smith and other swimmers who are accused of using drugs.

Lawyers by profession, the respective heads of Fina, the world swimming body, and LEN, Europe's governing organisation, agreed that the rules of the sport, as they stand, have allowed cheats to escape punishment. Incidents involving Smith in Ireland in the past 12 months had now forced the sport's administrators to rethink and redraft their rules on dope testing.

It was in 1994 that swimming's credibility gap became a chasm when, after they had destroyed the record books at the world championships, seven Chinese swimmers later tested positive. Following two decades of steroid-fuelled dominance in the pool by East Germany, this only served to confirm long-held fears that swimming was riddled with drugs.

Harm Beyer, secretary of LEN and chairman of Fina's doping commission, is certain that the problem is far from eradicated. 'Even now,' says the German, a criminal judge by profession, 'swimming is not free of drugs.'

Swimming's China syndrome brought about the introduction of out-of-competition testing, yet when Fina drafted its rules, it did such a bad job that it failed to include any sanction against swimmers who avoid or evade the testers.

> **'I accuse everyone concerned – from the top sports officials to the coaches and athletes – because while they say they are against drugs, when it comes to applying sanctions, we all become cowards'**

'As the rules stand, we have no power,' said Beyer yesterday. 'If a tester calls at a swimmer's home and they give a sample, the athlete might be caught positive if they have been using drugs. But the cheaters know they could walk out of their front door and refuse the test, and there's nothing we can do.'

The testing history of Smith, now competing under her married name of De Bruin, over the past three years has been chequered and caused disquiet on the poolside; not only from defeated rivals but even at the heart of Irish swimming.

In 1995, Irish ASA minutes recorded concern that they had no address for Smith, who had moved to Holland to train with her then boyfriend, Erik de Bruin, the former Dutch discus champion who was serving a four-year drugs ban from athletics.

At the beginning of 1996, Smith received a written warning from Fina about her non-availability for tests the previous year. In January this year, she was faxed another such letter. Yet on 3 February, when testers arrived at the Ballinteer home of Nick Sweeney, the Irish discus thrower, because Smith had informed them she would be staying there, they discovered she had checked into a Dublin hotel.

When Fina, who are spending £350,000 on random testing each year, discussed the case, they decided that under their rules no action could be taken that would survive a challenge in the courts.

Appropriately it is in Seville, the birthplace of Cervantes, that swimming chiefs have decided they no longer want to tilt at windmills. If passed at the Fina Congress next January, the rule drafted this week by Beyer could see swimmers banned if they miss two tests in succession.

'I am convinced that those who do drugs are always ahead of the testers,' said Beyer. 'I accuse everyone concerned – from the top sports officials to the coaches and athletes – because while they say they are against drugs, when it comes to applying sanctions, we all become cowards.'

Only Dagmar Hase, an admitted product of East Germany's drug-aided sports system, was able to halt Smith's relentless progress towards a third gold medal in the 400m freestyle on Thursday.

The following day, Smith said: 'I prove my innocence every time I take a dope test and every time it's negative.' When Beyer's new rule is passed, Smith will get an opportunity to prove her innocence more regularly.

# Testing procedures

## Doping control information from The UK Sports Council

Sportsmen and women may be tested for drugs at any time, on the day of competition or during training. All testing takes place at short, or no, notice. With competition testing, some governing bodies of sport specify a recommended selection procedure for competitors. For example, new records will only be ratified with a negative test.

Whether an athlete is selected for testing during training or competition, the procedure is the same.

### 1 Notifying the athlete

After an event or during training, in the UK, the competitor will be notified by a UK Sports Council Independent Sampling Officer (ISO) that they have been selected for a drug test. Where appropriate, the competitor will be allowed to complete their training session. With out-of-competition testing, the competitor may be given short, or no, notice.

### 2 Reporting for testing

A chaperone accompanies each competitor to be tested to the Doping Control Station waiting room. Sealed, non-alcoholic drinks are available, alongside reading material. All competitors are entitled to have a representative (from his/her sport's national governing body) present.

### 3 Selecting a collection vessel

When the competitor is ready to provide a sample of urine, he/she is asked to select a sample collection vessel.

### 4 Providing a sample under supervision

The competitor must remove sufficient clothing so that the ISO can directly observe the competitor providing the urine sample into the collection vessel. When the competitor has provided the required amount of urine – generally 100ml – he/she must return directly to the Doping Control Station administration room. Only the competitor should handle the sample.

### 5 Selecting the sample containers

The competitor will now be asked to select a pair of pre-sealed bottle containers.

### 6 Breaking the security seals

The competitor will be invited to break the security seals

### 7 Dividing the sample

The competitor will then be asked to divide his/her sample between the A and B sample bottles, putting approximately two-thirds of the sample into the A bottle and a minimum of 30ml into the B bottle.

### 8 Sealing the samples

The ISO ensures that the bottles have been tightly sealed by checking the bottle tops. The competitor is then invited to select two numbered seals and to seal the A and B packs.

### 9 Recording the information

The ISO records the bottle code and seal numbers on the Sample Collection Form: this information is checked by the competitor. The competitor is then asked to declare any medications that they he/she taken in the previous week.

### 10 Certifying the information

The ISO then asks the competitor (and their representative if present) to check all the information on the Sample Collection Form and, if satisfied, to sign the form. The ISO will also check and sign the form. The ISO provides the competitor with a copy of the Sample Collection

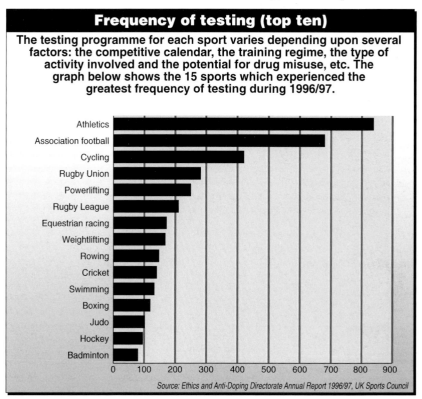

**Frequency of testing (top ten)**

The testing programme for each sport varies depending upon several factors: the competitive calendar, the training regime, the type of activity involved and the potential for drug misuse, etc. The graph below shows the 15 sports which experienced the greatest frequency of testing during 1996/97.

*Source: Ethics and Anti-Doping Directorate Annual Report 1996/97, UK Sports Council*

Form and the competitor is free to go.

## 11 Transferring the samples to the laboratory

The samples – in their sealed transit containers – are then sent to an accredited laboratory by a secure chain of custody for analysis. The laboratory receives the copy of the Sample Collection Form which details only the sample, seal numbers and the competitor's medications. No other information is provided which might allow the competitor to be identified.

## 12 Reporting the analytical result

Following laboratory analysis of the competitor's A sample, if no banned substances are found, a negative result will be reported to the relevant sport governing body and the B sample destroyed. This report is usually available within 10 days of the sample collection. If required, results can be made available within 24 hours during a major competition. If banned substances are found, the governing body is notified of the finding. The governing body then notifies the competitor.

In the case of a positive test, the procedure is generally as follows:
a) the competitor may be suspended from competition while the reason for the presence of the banned substance is considered.
The competitor is then entitled to a second analysis of the urine sample in the B bottle which the competitor (and/or a representative) may observe, plus an opportunity to present his/her case.
b) a decision will be taken. This may include suspension from competition for a given period, or even, in some cases, a lifetime ban.
c) every competitor is, however, entitled to appeal against the decision reached.

These procedures have been developed to ensure security and fairness in drug testing. Competitors can, of course, refuse to be tested. However, such a refusal is considered as though the urine sample gave a positive result.

[A detailed list of the classes of drugs which are banned by the International Olympic Committee (IOC) is available from the UK Sports Council. Those 'over the counter' preparations which may be taken for common ailments (such as hayfever, asthma, etc.) and which are permitted under the doping regulations of the IOC are listed in the UK Sports Councils' *Doping Control information booklet*, number 4.]
• The above is an extract from *Testing Procedures – A Guide for Competitors and Officials* produced by the UK Sports Council. See page 41 for address details.

*© UK Sports Council*

## Misuse of Drugs Act 1971

### Prosecution and punishment of offences

| Section Creating Offence | General nature of offence | Mode of prosecution | Punishment | | | |
|---|---|---|---|---|---|---|
| | | | Class A drug involved | Class B drug involved | Class C drug involved | General |
| Section 4(2)... | Production, or being concerned in the production, or a controlled drug | (a) Summary.. | 6 months or £5,000, or both. | 6 months or £5,000, or both. | 3 months or £500, or both. | |
| | | (b) On indictment | Life or a fine, or both | 14 years or a fine, or both | 5 years or a fine, or both | |
| Section 4(3)... | Supplying or offering to supply a controlled drug or being concerned in the doing of either activity by another. | (a) Summary.. | 6 months or £5,000, or both. | 6 months or £5,000, or both. | 3 months or £500, or both. | |
| | | (b) On indictment | Life or a fine, or both | 14 years or a fine, or both | 5 years or a fine, or both | |
| Section 5(2)... | Having possession of a controlled drug | (a) Summary.. | 6 months or £5,000, or both. | 3 months or £500, or both. | 3 months or £200, or both. | |
| | | (b) On indictment | 7 years or a fine, or both | 5 years or a fine, or both | 2 years or a fine, or both | |
| Section 5(3)... | Having possession of a controlled drug with intent to supply it to another | (a) Summary.. | 6 months or £5,000, or both. | 6 months or £5,000, or both. | 3 months or £500, or both. | |
| | | (b) On indictment | Life or a fine, or both | 14 years or a fine, or both | 5 years or a fine, or both | |
| Section 6(2)... | Cultivation of cannabis plant ... | (a) Summary.. | — | — | — | 6 months or £5,000, or both. |
| | | (b) On indictment | — | — | — | 14 years or a fine, or both |
| Section 8... | Being the occupier, or concerned in the management, of premises and permitting or suffering certain activities to take place there. | (a) Summary.. | 6 months or £5,000, or both. | 6 months or £5,000, or both. | 3 months or £500, or both. | |
| | | (b) On indictment | 14 years or a fine, or both | 14 years or a fine, or both | 5 years or a fine, or both | |

*Source: The Football Association*

# Drugs war is not so futile

**Michele Verroken, of the UK Sports Council (UKSC), responds to allegations that Britain's anti-doping measures have become a waste of time and money**

Tony Ward recently painted a picture of the war on dope cheats as a futile and costly witch-hunt with dope-testers akin to latter-day religious zealots on a crusade to spread their gospel whatever the cost. The British Athletic Federation's former public relations chief, writing in these pages two weeks ago, certainly raised some interesting issues about drug misuse and the mechanisms used to control the problem. What he omitted to consider fully, however, was the crux of this key issue – that of an athlete's right to participate in drug-free sport, competing in an ethical sporting environment free from the pressure to use drugs.

Perhaps it would be useful at this point to examine the approach currently adopted in the UK and clarify some important issues.

The doping-control programme in the UK is run through the United Kingdom Sports Council. This independent service for governing bodies of sport and sports organisations was introduced in 1988. Far from carrying out a crusade, our approved sampling officers are dedicated professionals – as is evident from the response of many athletes with whom they come into contact. The procedures they follow are designed to protect the integrity and security of the samples they collect.

If the price that an athlete has to pay is to provide a urine sample, when requested, and by doing so continue to demonstrate that the vast majority of sport is clean, is that too high a price?

The result of the drug-testing programmes so far in the UK show that over 98 per cent of samples are negative. Elite athletes have themselves endorsed and accepted the necessity for testing, and some 85 per cent of them expressed confidence in the UK's system in research carried out by the UK Sports Council in 1995. Indeed, Diane Modahl herself refers in her book to the high standard of 'chain of custody' documentation in the UK.

> *If the price that an athlete has to pay is to provide a urine sample, when requested, and by doing so continue to demonstrate that the vast majority of sport is clean, is that too high a price?*

I agree with Tony Ward, though, that there is room for improvement in many areas, and, on this count, the UKSC cannot be accused of inaction or complacency. The UKSC – backed by Government support – are key partners in developing international agreements aimed at progressing and improving standards. In collaboration with Australia, Canada, New Zealand and Norway, we have developed a quality-control system for dope-testing procedures and will seek an internationally agreed standard for it over the coming year. This system covers everything from the design of the testing programmes, selecting and testing procedures, to results, management and treatment of athletes.

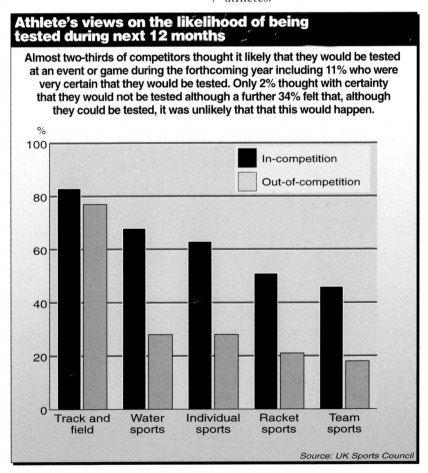

**Athlete's views on the likelihood of being tested during next 12 months**

Almost two-thirds of competitors thought it likely that they would be tested at an event or game during the forthcoming year including 11% who were very certain that they would be tested. Only 2% thought with certainty that they would not be tested although a further 34% felt that, although they could be tested, it was unlikely that that this would happen.

%

In-competition
Out-of-competition

Track and field | Water sports | Individual sports | Racket sports | Team sports

*Source: UK Sports Council*

We are also conscious that there is considerable room for a move towards greater consistency in the disciplinary procedures. For that reason we are working with governing bodies to review their constitutions and put in place effective doping procedures. This has not proved to be a simple task. We have, however, invested in excess of £50,000 to help get it right.

Having attended a range of hearings as an observer as well as an expert witness, I am in no doubt that sport in the UK would benefit from an effective dispute resolution system. A system independent of the sport, headed by an expert panel, would help all concerned avoid the costly and complex legal challenges we have seen to date. The UKSC are actively advocating an independent sport's dispute resolution system, combined with a fair and informed review process. For this or any other system to succeed, athletes must have total confidence that they will receive a fair hearing.

Education is, of course, a fundamental element in spreading the anti-doping gospel. If we can succeed in raising the question of sporting values early in an athlete's career, then we can help them to see that you can succeed without drugs, and that drugs cannot replace skill. This should create and sustain positive anti-drug attitudes. Education programmes should not be aimed at athletes alone but must include coaches and all those who provide support services to athletes.

Without an all-round commitment to drug-free sport, there is the very real danger that, for example, the coach who runs out of ideas, but not enthusiasm, may indirectly promote drug abuse to improve or maintain performance.

Education is everyone's responsibility. Well-informed and consistent messages will endorse athletes' perceptions about drug-free sport. Indeed, Tony Ward's suggestion that an athlete has 24 hours to provide a urine sample is an unfortunate case of misinformation. Athletes are required to provide the sample as soon as possible. Justifiable delays are treated with discretion, but are tightly monitored.

---

*The result of the drug-testing programmes so far in the UK show that over 98 per cent of samples are negative*

---

As sport generally becomes more professional, the management of drug abuse and drug testing must reflect the situation. It is effectively becoming an employee screening programme.

When an athlete's career is at stake, there is no room for amateur management. Hence the UKSC make no apologies for protecting athletes' rights to participate in drug-free sport and we look for the co-operation of those involved in sport at all levels to help us achieve this aim.

• Michele Verroken is the UK Sports Council's director of ethics and anti-doping.

© *The Observer*
*February, 1997*

## History of doping control

1865 – First reports of doping in modern sport

1955 – 25 urine tests performed on cyclists in one race in France; 5 were positive

1959 – Association Nationale d'Education Physique (ANEP) formed a doping commission in France

1962 – The International Olympic Committee (IOC) passed a resolution against doping

1963 – Council of Europe adopted a clear definition of doping

1965 – Professor Arnold Beckett of the Chelsea College of Science and Technology, London University, analysed samples collected from the Tour of Britain cycle race. The Sports Council formed a working party on Drug Abuse in sport.

1966 – Chelsea College was responsible for testing samples at the Football World Cup

1968 – Drugs testing instituted generally at both Winter and Summer Olympic Games

1969 – Professor Raymond Brooks began research at St Thomas' on new testing techniques backed by the Sports Council

1970 – Drugs tests first instituted at Commonwealth Games (not steroids)

1976 – First steroid tests introduced at Olympic Games

1978 – The Drug Control and Teaching Centre established at Chelsea College, University of London, with financial support from the Sports Council

1979 – The Council of Europe adopted a recommendation urging states to combat drug abuse in sport

1983 – The Sports Council called for the expansion of random drug tests in British sport

1985 – The Sports Council required that senior governing bodies of sport in Britain introduce drug testing

1986 – The Sports Council purchased a Mobile Sampling Unit to enable the random collection of samples at any event (indoors or outdoors) by independent sampling officers

1987 – HRH Princess Anne opened new accommodation for the Drug Control and Teaching Centre at King's College, Chelsea

1988 – The Sports Council introduced a revised system of doping control incorporating modified procedures for sample collection in and out of competition using independent Sampling Officers

© *UK Sports Council*

# Drugs

**Vital information for everyone involved in Rugby League**

## Message from Emma Rosewarne, Administration Executive

This information is designed for use by all players, coaches and administrators involved in professional Rugby League at whatever level. The importance of the information contained in it cannot be over-estimated.

Drug scandals have an extreme adverse effect on any sport in which they occur. At this crucial stage of its history, as professional Rugby League switches to summer with the eyes of the world focused on the beginnings of Super League, our sport cannot afford to be involved in the bad publicity which is associated with a positive drugs test.

Players have a responsibility to themselves and to their team-mates and opponents to ensure that they know how to avoid banned drugs. Coaches, too, must take responsibility for educating players in their charge and providing them with the right advice. Club administrators must also be aware that this is an issue which is relevant to them, and provide informed support to their playing and coaching staff.

The Rugby Football League has made a public commitment to eradicating substance abuse from the game, and are prepared to back this up with positive and radical action. It is the job of clubs and players to ensure that the governing body does not need to fulfil this commitment.

Emma L. Rosewarne
Administration Executive
The Rugby Football League
October 1996

## Doping control programme

Doping is defined as the taking or use of substances or the participation in doping methods prohibited by the Rugby Football League. In addition, assisting or inciting others to contravene doping regulations is also considered a doping offence.

The Rugby Football League condemns the use of doping – it is cheating, it is contrary to the spirit of fair competition and puts the health of the competitor at risk.

The Rugby Football League, in conjunction with the UK Sports Council, has developed a doping control programme which has two key elements:
- Testing
- Education

---

*The Rugby Football League condemns the use of doping – it is cheating, it is contrary to the spirit of fair competition and puts the health of the competitor at risk*

---

### Testing

Testing is carried out in two main ways:
i) Competition testing – Players are selected for testing at the end of a match.
ii) Out-of-competition testing – Players are selected for testing at training sessions at either club or national level or at any other time or place.

### Education

The League expects all clubs to hold educational sessions at least once a season. In addition, the League produces information like this article and runs poster campaigns in dressing rooms.

● The above is an extract from *Drugs – Vital information for everyone involved in Rugby League*, produced by the Rugby Football League. See page 41 for address details.

© *Rugby Football League
October, 1996*

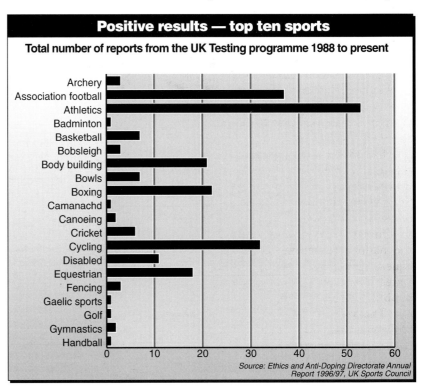

**Positive results — top ten sports**

Total number of reports from the UK Testing programme 1988 to present

Archery
Association football
Athletics
Badminton
Basketball
Bobsleigh
Body building
Bowls
Boxing
Camanachd
Canoeing
Cricket
Cycling
Disabled
Equestrian
Fencing
Gaelic sports
Golf
Gymnastics
Handball

0   10   20   30   40   50   60

*Source: Ethics and Anti-Doping Directorate Annual Report 1996/97, UK Sports Council*

# How talk can beat a ban

## Neil Wilson on stars who buck system

**G**uilty until proven innocent. That is the assumption sport makes when a competitor refuses to take a drugs test. The punishment for those who refuse tests matches exactly those shown by tests to have committed the crime. Two years in most sports, four in some and life in a few.

Athletics in Britain once banned a very ordinary club runner for four years when he gave up trying to provide a sample after nearly an hour for fear that he would be late for work.

But that hard-line attitude is unusual. A lot more get away with it without anybody knowing of their refusal. Some change to another sport or to a different federation within the same sport. Some retire quietly. And most talk their way out of it.

The most famous was John Ngugi, an Olympic champion and five-time world cross country champion. The Kenyan, faced on his own farm with the arrival of a British testing officer demanding an out-of-competition test, refused.

Ngugi argued that he had not understood the demand and the Kenyans refused to ban him. The IAAF, athletics' world body, did initially but lifted it when he appealed.

In Britain boxing announced that it had accepted the explanation of one of its own who refused a UK Sports Council test in 1996-97. It never said what it was.

In the same 12-month period the national governing bodies of equestrianism and hockey found 'extenuating circumstances' for not punishing refusers.

That year 15 refused in Britain. Only one, a weightlifter, was forced to serve a ban. Two of the 13 who refused in 1996-97 received no more than written warnings.

It may explain why the number refusing is increasing. In the last 10 years of testing 86 have refused the request to fill the sample bottle, almost a third in the last two years.

Ngugi's explanation would be insufficient in Britain now. All competitors are well aware of the risk from testers from the UK Sports Council, who act as samplers on behalf of governing bodies. It is the police, acting on behalf ends with a test. The governing bodies act as their own judge and jury. Phil Tufnell's fate lies not with those who tested him but with his peers.

Olympic sports led the way in the mid-1970s with testing programmes, originally only at competitions but later at training sessions.

These are financed by the UK Sports Council.

Commercial sports have followed in the last 10 years, paying the UK Sports Council to do the job for them. Testing in soccer is common now. A total of 500 tests on clubs in the Premiership and Nationwide leagues were made in 1996-97, most at training grounds.

Cricket conducted 140 tests during the summer of 1996 and estimate that about the same will have been carried out this year. But they took place at only 31 games.

### Roll of dishonour

1967 – Briton Tommy Simpson dies during Tour de France. He took amphetamines.

1969 – Dutch decathlete Eduard de Noorlander is first athlete disqualified for taking steroids.

1972 – First Olympic gold medallist, US swimmer Rick deMont, disqualified after testing positive to ephedrine.

1987 – German heptathlete Birgit Dressel dies from allergic reaction to drugs.

1988 – Ben Johnson tests positive to steroids at Seoul. Banned for two years.

1990 – Ritchie Griffiths is first British rugby player caught taking steroids.

1991 – Diego Maradona banned for 15 months for cocaine use.

1994 – Maradona expelled from the World Cup for testing positive to ephedrine.

1995 – Jamie Bloem first British rugby league player banned for steroids.

1996 – Sussex player Ed Giddings banned until 1998 for cocaine use.

© The Daily Mail,
September, 1997

# Tarnished gold

**Davies leads fight to strip cheats of medals. By Neil Wilson**

Britain raised its standard for a fight to rid sport's history books of the East Germans who shamed it yesterday with the rallying cry: Gold for Sharron.

The case of Sharron Davies, deprived of an Olympic gold medal 17 years ago by a German exposed now as a drug-taker, will spearhead a campaign across all sports to have East Germans stripped of medals and records.

Others who may benefit by getting medals or records that drug-taking East Germans were awarded include Davies' swimming friend Margaret Kelly and athletes Kathy Cook, Roger Black and Iwan Thomas.

Support for the bid to persuade sport's world governing bodies and the International Olympic Committee to cleanse its records came yesterday from the United Kingdom Sports Council and the British Olympic Association.

More crucial support came from Professor Werner Franke, an internationally-renowned expert on cell and molecular biology whose research into secret East German government files has exposed institutionalised drug-taking among the nation's sports teams over 25 years.

Franke promised to make the documents he has discovered in the files of the former East German Ministry for State Security (Stasi) available to prove that athletes, swimmers, weightlifters and bobsleighers who were winning Olympic titles were on drugs. Yesterday, in London, he produced state documents which confirm that all the great East Germans were, as he called it, 'loaded', including several still competing. 'You never saw a blue-shirted (East German) athlete who won anything who was not on drugs,' he said.

Among those whom Stasi documents confirm were put on drugs by team doctors and coaches was Petra Schneider who, at 17, beat Davies in the 1980 Olympic 400 metres individual medley in a world record time which has never been surpassed by another swimmer.

Schneider recently admitted that she was a drug-taker when she launched a civil case with other former East German swimmers seeking compensation for the damage done to their health from former team officials.

Davies said yesterday: 'How can world records or medals that were set or won stay in place now the truth is known? The names of those individuals and the countries they represented which so often condoned their cheating should be removed from public sight.

'Having suffered directly at the hands of cheats – and there is no other word for athletes who take these substances – I feel very emotional about this subject. All my career I now know I was swimming against Eastern-bloc swimmers whom we now have irrefutable evidence were on a drug programme devised for them from above.

'I don't hold those swimmers in contempt but I do the governing bodies and officials who sanctioned it and used the swimmers' honours and glories for their own propaganda purposes.

---

*'How can world records that were set or medals won stay in place now the truth is known?'*

---

'It was at the expense of other innocent athletes who were being told constantly that the cheats were being caught. We now know differently.

'What retribution or compensation is there? For me that moment of glory is lost for ever. But this strengthens my resolve and determination to get something done. To do nothing is to say it was OK.'

Davies' case has been taken up with the BOA by the Amateur Swimming Association. Simon Clegg, the BOA's general secretary, said: 'Naturally we will support any of our governing bodies or competitors in this if there is firm evidence.'

Other British swimmers who would have won gold medals at the 1980 Olympics but for East Germans since exposed were butterfly swimmer Ann Osgerby and the 4x100m medley relay of Kelly, Osgerby, Helen Jameson and June Croft.

Cook, a sprinter who was Britain's most bemedalled woman athlete before Sally Gunnell, finished second in the 200m at the 1982 European Championships to East German Barbara Wockel, another whom Franke outed at yesterday's drugs seminar.

Cook would also have won Olympic silver and bronze and a world relay gold and a world individual silver medal but for Wockel and another exposed cheat, Marita Koch, whose world 400m record still stands.

'It's laughable,' said Franke yesterday.

Another outed by Franke is Thomas Schoenlebe, an East German who still holds the European 400m record which would otherwise have gone first to Roger Black and now to Iwan Thomas.

© *The Daily Mail*
*September, 1997*

# Lifters 'not pulling weight' on drug tests

## By Duncan Mackay

British weightlifting has been warned by the UK Sports Council that funding could be stopped if the sport does not get its house in order over drug testing. The council is angry that 31 per cent of the lifters it approached for random testing during the past year were unavailable.

'We have been in deep discussions with the British Amateur Weightlifting Association about the inadequacy of the testing programme,' said Michelle Verroken, director of the UKSC ethics and anti-doping directorate. 'We want to see improvement.' Verroken is due to meet senior officials of the BAWLA this weekend, when she will warn them they face losing their annual £100,000 grant unless things get better. It would almost certainly mean the collapse of the small organisation if its main source of funding was lost.

'This is not a case of applying Big Brother tactics,' said Howard Wells, the chief executive of the UKSC. 'We want them to face their responsibilities. Withdrawal of funds is very much a last resort.'

The figures are revealed in the UKSC's ethics and anti-doping directorate annual report for 1996-97 released yesterday. It shows that 4,469 samples from 47 sports were analysed by King's College, London. Only two per cent were reported as suspect, the same as last year, but anabolic agents were discovered in 27 samples, as against the previous year's 15.

Anabolic agents, such as steroids, increase strength and enable athletes to train harder because they recover more quickly. Most of the failures during the past year have come in strength events, such as weightlifting and powerlifting.

---

*Anabolic agents, such as steroids, increase strength and enable athletes to train harder because they recover more quickly*

---

The findings are a surprise as it was assumed competitors seeking chemical assistance had switched to more state-of-the-art performance-enhancing drugs, such as the human growth hormone for which there is no reliable test.

The report comes a few weeks after the International Amateur Athletic Federation's decision to cut the length of suspension for a first offence for anabolic steroids from four years to two.

'This seems to be a blatant disregard for the rules,' said Verroken.

'Penalties for anabolic steroids in many sports are being reduced. Sport may need to rethink whether there is any deterrence factor.' Overall, though, the number of offences discovered by the £1 million programme last year dropped from 84 to 82. 'It is a great testament to the integrity of our competitors that 98 per cent tested negative,' said Verroken.

Jonny Searle, the 1992 Olympic coxed pairs gold medallist, said the figures proved that a *Panorama* programme claiming, on the eve of last year's Atlanta Games, that 75 per cent of Britain's teams were using drugs was wholly inaccurate.

Verroken had special praise for the time and effort football had invested in drug testing during the last year. They carried out 480 tests, second only to athletics, which did 685.

# Fear over drug cheats

**British sport could be in a drugs crisis if the current ban of four years is reduced to two**

British sport could be heading for a drugs crisis if the current ban on offenders of four years is reduced to two.

The UK Sports Council's director of anti-doping, Michelle Verroken said yesterday: 'It becomes a calculated risk for the athletes if they only have to miss two years competition, because of drugs.

'We need to have a firm deterrent in place so they won't want to do it otherwise there is no real reason why they don't.' Verroken has received strong support in her criticism of the IOC decision to allow convicted athletes back after a two-year suspension. President of the British Athletic Federation and former Olympic champion Mary Peters backed her initiative.

Peters said: 'With all the pressure on today's athletes, there needs to be something in place to show them the consequences of their actions.

'I was so naive when I was competing but there also wasn't the sheer level of financial incentives there are now.

'If you can win a gold medal then an awful lot of money could follow and that is a huge temptation,' she added.

Verroken believes that the increasing professionalism of sport means that without firm controls there could be a rapid rise in positive tests.

'With all the changes going on in sport and athletes stretching themselves that much more, without a strong message there could be problems.

'The best example is drink-driving. When the law wasn't harsh there were more people doing it, now there has been a massive drop in the drink-driving rate,' added Verroken.

Britain can boast the impressive statistic of less than two per cent of athletes testing positive but Verroken fears the worst if the current ban is lowered.

'Without a sound punishment, the athletes may decide to go for the calculated risk and they won't care if they get banned because they are only out for a short time.

'The potential is there for problems.'

© *The Mirror*
*October, 1997*

# Steroid misuse shows increase

## By John Goodbody

Positive tests for anabolic steroids in the United Kingdom have risen by 80 per cent over the past year. Although only 2 per cent of about 4,000 samples analysed under the drugs-testing programme run by King's College London, proved positive – about the same as the previous year – anabolic agents were discovered in 27 of the samples as against 15 in the previous 12 months.

The findings are especially surprising because there is a suspicion that some offenders have switched to substances that cannot yet be detected.

When the United Kingdom Sports Council (UKSC), which administers the scheme at a yearly cost of more than £1 million, releases the latest statistics today, the use of hormone drugs, particularly among weightlifters and powerlifters, will show a sharp increase. This may help to persuade the Government to make the possession of anabolic steroids illegal, unless used under medical supervision.

'We are focusing on those areas of sport where there is still determination to use drugs and where some competitors are obviously not good enough without them,' Michele Verroken, director of the UKSC's ethics and anti-doping directorate, said yesterday. The total number of doping offences discovered during the period under review was 82, compared with 84 in 1995-96.

'It is a great testament to the integrity of our competitors that 98 per cent tested negative,' Verroken said. 'This is a result that confirms that the vast majority of them are competing drug-free.' Tomorrow, leading sportsmen and sportswomen will attend a national seminar on drugs and sport in London. Surveys have shown that many of them want life bans for anyone caught taking hormone drugs, although the trend internationally is to reduce penalties.

Six weeks ago, the International Amateur Athletic Federation reduced the length of suspension for a first offence from four years to two, because of the fear of legal actions from banned athletes.

© *Times Newspapers Limited*
*September, 1997*

# ADDITIONAL RESOURCES

You might like to contact the following organisations for further information. Due to the increasing cost of postage, many organisations cannot respond to enquiries unless they receive a stamped, addressed envelope.

**Institute for the Study of Drug Dependence (ISDD)**
Waterbridge House
32-36 Loman Street
London, SE1 0EE
Tel: 0171 928 1211
Fax: 0171 928 1771
To disseminate information and promote research on all aspects of drug misuse.

**International Olympic Committee Medical Commission**
Chateau de Vidy
Case Postale 356
1001 Lausanne
Switzerland
Tel: 00 41 21 624 6166
Fax: 00 41 21 621 6216

**Lifeline**
101-103 Oldham Street
Manchester, M4 1LW
Tel: 0161 839 2054
Fax: 0161 834 5903
A harm reduction agency offering advice, information and support to drug users, their family and friends. Also runs daytime services, a parent's service, a prison and outreach services.

**National Coaching Foundation (NCF)**
114 Cardigan Road
Headingley
Leeds, LS6 3BJ
Tel: 0113 274 4802
Fax 0113 275 5019
Publishes *Coaching Focus* and *Super Coach. Coaching Focus* is published three times a year and may be subscribed to through the National Association of Sports Coaches (NASC). For further details on *Coaching Focus*, the NCF or NASC please ring 0113 231 1310, membership services.

**Release**
388 Old Street
London, EC1V 9LT
Tel: 0171 729 5255
Fax: 0171 729 2599
A national charity offering a range of services to people concerned with drug use. Produces a series of inexpensive factsheets and leaflets on different drug types i.e. cocaine, ecstasy, cannabis, heroin etc. Also has a 24-hour helpline (0171 603 8654). Offers training and education programmes as well as legal advice.

**Sports Council for Wales**
Sophia Gardens
Cardiff, CF1 9SW
Tel: 01222 300500
Fax: 01222 300600
Produces a wide range of information relating to the illegal use of drugs in sport: booklets, leaflets, posters, advice cards, reports and videos. Ask for their publications list.

**The Advisory Council on Alcohol and Drug Education (TACADE)**
1 Hulme Place
The Crescent
Salford
Greater Manchester, M5 4QA
Tel: 0161 745 8925
Fax: 0161 745 8923
Publish a wide range of factsheets on drug-related issues in their *Basic Facts* series.

**The English Sports Council**
16 Upper Woburn Place
London, WC1H 0QP
Tel: 0171 273 1500
Fax: 0171 383 5740
Produces a wide range of information relating to the illegal use of drugs in sport: booklets, leaflets, posters, advice cards, reports and videos. Ask for their publications list.

**The Football Association**
Lilleshall Hall National Sports
Centre
Newport
Shropshire, TF10 9AT
Tel: 01952 605 928
Fax: 01952 825 476

**The Referees Association**
1 Westhill Road
Coundon
Coventry, CV6 2AD
Tel: 01203 601701

**The Rugby Football League**
Red Hall
Red Hall Lane
Leeds, LS17 8NB
Tel: 0113 232 9111
Fax: 0113 232 3666

**The Scottish Sports Council**
Caledonia House
South Gyle
Edinburgh, EH12 9DQ
Tel: 0131 317 7200
Fax: 0131 317 7202
Produces a wide range of information relating to the illegal use of drugs in sport: booklets, leaflets, posters, advice cards, reports and videos. Ask for their publications list.

**UK Sports Council**
Walkden House
3-10 Melton Street
London, NW1 2EB
Tel: 0171 380 8030
Fax: 0171 380 8035
Produces a wide range of information relating to the illegal use of drugs in sport: booklets, leaflets, posters, advice cards, reports and videos. Ask for their publications list.

# INDEX

# ACKNOWLEDGEMENTS

The publisher is grateful for permission to reproduce the following material.

While every care has been taken to trace and acknowledge copyright, the publisher tenders its apology for any accidental infringement or where copyright has proved untraceable. The publisher would be pleased to come to a suitable arrangement in any such case with the rightful owner.

### Chapter One: Drugs in Sport

*Consider the consequences*, © The Football Association, *The medical effects of steroid abuse*, © National Coaching Foundation, *Drugs, doping and young people*, © Arena, April 1995, *Drug cheats still one lap ahead*, © The Observer, July 1996, *The Mr Cleans face an uphill struggle*, © The Financial Times, August 1996, *How drug runners slip through the net*, © The Observer, July 1996, *Scientist supports legalising steroids*, © The Independent, August 1996, *How an innocent lunchtime bagel could ruin a promising career*, © The Independent, February 1997, *Anabolic steroids*, © The UK Sports Council, *Cheats prosper from soft pedalling hard drugs*, © The Observer, April 1997, *Norway, France, UK wage on drugs cheats*, © The European, September 1996, *Message in bottle*, © The Observer, February 1997, *Olympic chief calls for drug leniency*, © The Daily Mail, December 1996, *World scientists seek to beat drug cheats*, © The European, April 1997, *Testing programme*, © UK Sports Council, *The professional's feedback*, © The Football Association, *Skin up and you're off*, © The Football Association, *The race against drugs*, © International Herald Tribune, August 1997, *Games scandal of drug they call Silent Speed*, © The Daily Express, August 1996, *Testing programme by sport*, © UK Sports Council, *The non-medical social use of drugs*, © National Coaching Foundation, *Bromantan is Russians' 'rocket fuel'*, © Independent, August 1996.

### Chapter Two: Drugs Testing

*Doping in sport*, © UK Sports Council, *Sanctions*, © UK Sports Council, *Doping control in sport*, © UK Sports Council, *The 1996/97 testing programme*, © UK Sports Council, *Drug tests on 9-year-olds*, © The Guardian, June 1997, *Battle hots up in drugs war*, © The Observer, August 1997, *Testing procedures*, © National Coaching Foundation, *Frequency to testing (top ten)*, © UK Sports Council, *Misuse of Drugs Act 1971*, © The Football Association, *Drugs war is not so futile*, © The Observer, February 1997, *Likelihood of being tested during next 12 months*, © UK Sports Council, *Drugs*, © Rugby Football League, October 1996, *Positive results – top ten sports*, © UK Sports Council, *How talk can beat a ban*, © The Daily Mail, September 1997, *Tarnished gold*, © The Daily Mail, September 1997, *Lifters 'not pulling weight' on drug tests*, © The Guardian, September 1997, *Fear over drug cheats*, © The Mirror, October 1997, *Steroid misuse shows increase*, © Times Newspapers Limited, September 1997.

### Photographs and illustrations:

Pages 2, 12, 28: Michaela Bloomfield, pages 4, 10, 25: Andrew Smith, pages 6, 8, 9, 14, 17, 30, 39: Ken Pyne.

Craig Donnellan
Cambridge
January, 1998